The Golden Age of
Children's Television
Quiz Book

Geoff Tibballs

TITAN BOOKS
LONDON

THE GOLDEN AGE OF CHILDREN'S TELEVISION QUIZ BOOK
ISBN 1 85286 450 8

Published by
Titan Books Ltd
19 Valentine Place
London SE1 8QH

First edition October 1992
10 9 8 7 6 5 4 3 2 1

British Library Cataloguing-in-Publication Data. A catalogue record for this book is available from the British Library.

Text copyright © Geoff Tibballs 1992.
This edition copyright © Titan Books Ltd 1992.
All rights reserved.

ACKNOWLEDGEMENTS

The author would like to thank the following for kindly supplying photographs:

British Sky Broadcasting, Channel 4, Matthew Corbett, Jan and Vlasta Dalibor, Jon Keeble at ITC Entertainment, Bobbie Mitchell at BBC Picture Library.

Thanks also to the staff of the ITC Library, Brompton Road, for their customary help and efficiency and to everyone at Titan Books for still believing that there really is such a place as Trumpton. This book is respectfully dedicated to all those people who, after reading *The Golden Age of Children's Television*, asked me: "Do you remember Squiddly Diddly?" I do. And he's here.

Typeset and designed by Titan Studio, London.
Printed and bound in Great Britain by Cox and Wyman Ltd, Reading, Berkshire.

Contents

Introduction

It's happened to us all at some time. Sat around a table at an important meeting, faced with a jug of water, a plate of Rich Teas and a sea of important executive faces. But you can't concentrate – there's a nagging thought that you can't get out of your mind. It has nothing to do with the matters being discussed around the table; not whether the corporate strategy is right or even whether the new company logo looks like a baboon's bottom. It is more fundamental than that. For what's bugging you is: What *were* the names of the twins in *The Woodentops*?

It all started the previous evening in the cafe when one of your friends proceeded to demonstrate the Spotty Dog walk. And as the staff cleared up, someone asked: "And who were the twins in *The Woodentops*?"

Well, thanks to this book, such great debates need haunt you no more. Within these pages lie over 1,000 puzzling posers relating to children's television in the fifties, sixties and early seventies. Everything you could possibly want to know is here – from the name of Ivor the Engine's driver to Penelope Pitstop's car. Plus there are crosswords, wordsearches and more trivia boxes than in the average John Motson commentary.

So, impress your friends with your new-found knowledge. This book may not cure baldness or remove those unmentionable stains, but it will make you a much sought-after fount of information – that is until you start boring the pants off everyone. Remember, there is a time and a place for revealing the identity of Precious Pup's owner.

Just to break up a few more friendships, I've even devised a points system so that you can have competitions to find out who is the real expert on, say, *Thunderbirds*. Each question has a letter in front of it. The A questions are relatively straightforward and are worth one point, the B questions are a little tougher and are worth two points and the C questions are real mind-bogglers, worth three. So tot up your totals when you come to check the answers at the back.

This is not only more than just another quiz book, it's more than £1.99. But look upon it as an investment for the future – it could change your life. Yes, this humble tome could even earn you that long-awaited promotion at work. For who knows, behind that gruff exterior and grey suit, your boss could be a closet Hammy Hamster fan...

1 Lady Penelope's FAB 20

First screened in 1965, Thunderbirds *remains the most popular of the Gerry and Sylvia Anderson Supermarionation series as new generations revel in the daring exploits of those stunted defenders of the Earth, International Rescue. The character of glamorous blonde Lady Penelope was based on Sylvia Anderson, although Sylvia was unaware of it at the time, while the voice of Lady P's Cockney ex-con chauffeur Parker was modelled on a waiter at a Berkshire pub frequented by the Andersons. Apparently, as he became increasingly flustered serving hungry customers, the poor man had a tendency to drop his 'H's, either altogether, into the wrong places, or maybe into the soup.*

A1 In what type of car was Lady Penelope driven around?

A2 What was its distinctive numberplate?

A3 How many Thunderbird craft are there?

A4 On which island does International Rescue have its secret headquarters?

A5 Who founded International Rescue?

A6 What is the name of the team's shy scientific genius?

A7 Which arch villain is the sworn enemy of International Rescue?

B8 Who is the pilot of Thunderbird 1?

B9 Who controls Thunderbird 2?

B10 Who mans Thunderbird 3?

B11 Who pilots Thunderbird 4?

B12 Who sits at the controls of space monitor Thunderbird 5?

B13 What is the name of International Rescue's special underground drilling machine?

C14 Who is Jeff Tracy's loyal manservant?

C15 What relation is the answer to number 7 to number 14? (Half will not do!)

C16 What is the name of International Rescue's blasting cannon, equipped with a laser beam?

C17 In what year is *Thunderbirds* supposedly set?

C18 Which actor provided the voice for Parker?

C19 What is Lady Penelope's surname?

C20 Which comedian and game show host lent his voice to a number of *Thunderbirds* characters?

FAMOUS THUNDERBIRDS FANS

- ☞ Prince Charles
- ☞ Mick Jagger
- ☞ Tony Curtis
- ☞ Roger Moore
- ☞ Tom Jones
- ☞ Roger Daltrey
- ☞ The Bee Gees
- ☞ Olivia Newton-John
- ☞ Des O'Connor
- ☞ Adam Faith
- ☞ Steve Wright
- ☞ Peter Cook
- ☞ Dudley Moore

2 The Gerry Anderson Tapes

A1 Which Gerry Anderson series features the law enforcing agency Spectrum?

A2 Which master of gobbledegook starred as a country vicar/secret agent in *The Secret Service*?

A3 Who was the sheriff of Four Feather Falls?

A4 Where was Torchy's battery-powered lamp situated?

A5 What were Twizzle's special powers?

B6 Which evil sea lord is the Stingray crew's great enemy?

B7 What was Joe 90's full name?

B8 To which land was Torchy sent by rocket?

B9 Who provided the speaking voice for Tex Tucker in *Four Feather Falls*?

B10 And who provided Tex's singing voice?

B11 Which former star of *Maigret* was the voice of Mac, Joe 90's guardian?

C12 Name four of the five angels in *Captain Scarlet and the Mysterons*.

C13 What does WASP stand for in *Stingray*?

C14 Who ran the Denison saloon in *Four Feather Falls*?

C15 In *Torchy*, what was the residence of King Dithers?

C16 What was the name of the white faced golliwog in *Twizzle*?

C17 Who was the vicar's housekeeper in *The Secret Service*?

C18 What machine did BIG RAT stand for in *Joe 90*?

C19 Who was the resident doctor in *Captain Scarlet and the Mysterons*?

C20 Who was Shane Weston's deputy in *Joe 90*?

3   **Happy Families**

Complete these TV partnerships:

A1   Bill and ___, the Flowerpot Men.
A2   Rag, Tag and ___.
A3   Andy Pandy, Looby Loo and ___.
A4   Tom and ___.
A5   Yogi Bear and ___.

B6   Augie Doggie and ___.
B7   Tich and ___.
B8   Roobarb and ___.
B9   Tingha and ___.
B10 Pixie and ___.

C11 Mary, Mungo and ___.
C12 Noah and ___.
C13 ___ and Montmorency.
C14 Bleep and ___.
C15 Crystal Tipps and ___.

4   From Book to Screen

A1 Which *Department S* star appeared in an adaptation of *A Tale of Two Cities*?

A2 Which future star of *The Sweeney* was Richmal Crompton's Just William in 1962?

A3 Which noted actress played Bobbie in the BBC's 1968 production of *The Railway Children*?

A4 Which famous bear in a scarf had his own ITV series?

A5 What sound does Noddy's car make?

B6 Who played Biggles in the 1960 ITV adaptation?

B7 Who created Paddington Bear?

B8 And what is Paddington's favourite food?

B9 Which actress took over from Judi Bowker in the 1972 ITV presentation of *The Adventures of Black Beauty*?

B10 Who wrote the Biggles books?

C11 Who introduced the BBC's *Tales from Dickens*?

C12 Which bane of Basil Fawlty's life once appeared in an adaptation of *The Secret Garden*?

C13 What part did Bernard Hepton play in the BBC's 1960's adaptation of *Great Expectations*?

C14 Which member of *Dad's Army* played Mr Micawber in the 1975 adaptation of *David Copperfield*?

C15 Which sixties pop star, who had a hit with 'Johnny Remember Me', played Ginger in the 1960 *Biggles* series?

5   Spot the Tune

From which children's TV themes do the following lyrics come?

A1 'Feared by the bad, loved by the good...'

A2 'So they loaded up the truck and they moved to Beverly...'

A3 'Tra-la-la, la-la-la, tra-la-la, la-la-la...'

A4 'Close friends get to call him TC...'

A5 'One for sorrow, two for joy, three for a girl and four for a boy...'

B6 'Let's go a-roving, a-roving, across the ocean-o...'

B7 'Time to go home, time to go home. Andy is waving goodbye, goodbye.'

B8 'People say we monkey around, but we're too busy singing, to put anybody down...'

B9 'Making good use of the things that we find, things that the everyday folks leave behind...'

C10 'It's you for me and me for you, just as one and one make two, it's us until forever...'

C11 'Faster than lightning, no one you see is smarter than he. And we know ___ lives in a world full of wonder, lying there under, under the sea.'

C12 'To adventure, bold adventure watch him go. There's no power on earth can stop what he's begun; with Bart and Gurth, he'll fight till he has won...'

C13 'They're creepy and they're kookie, mysterious and spooky, they're altogether ooky...'

6 The Trumpton Job Centre

Gordon Murray was one of the mainstays of BBC children's television during the Golden Age. He had already produced the ingenious Rubovia plays, featuring such characters as the King and Queen, the Lord Chamberlain and Mr Weatherspoon, and then in the sixties he invented the wonderful world of Camberwick Green, Trumpton *and* Chigley. *What a wonderful place Trumpton must have been to live in – no gangs roaming the streets, no unemployment, and no danger of The Krankies appearing there in summer season. What's more, there was a highly trained band of firefighters ready to deal with any emergency. All that was missing was a decent Chinese takeaway.*

Yes, everyone had a job at Camberwick Green, Trumpton and Chigley. But can you remember who did what? All the characters and occupations below are jumbled up. See if you can pair them off.

B1	Chippy Minton	milkman
B2	Nick Fisher	town clerk
B3	Mrs Dingle	chimney sweep
B4	Micky Murphy	postmistress
B5	Thomas Tripp	carpenter
B6	Mr Clamp	ice cream man
B7	Mrs Cobbit	bill poster
B8	Mr Platt	butler to Lord Belborough
B9	Mr Craddock	fishmonger
B10	Mr Brackett	baker
B11	Mr Carraway	rag and bone man
B12	Roger Varley	clockmaker
B13	Raggy Dan	park-keeper
B14	Mr Antonio	flower seller
B15	Mr Troop	greengrocer

FOUR FEATHER FALLS CHARACTERS

- Tex Tucker
- Dusty, Tex's dog
- Rocky, Tex's horse
- Ma Jones, the general store proprietor
- Marvin Jackson, the bank manager
- Dan Morse, the telegraphist
- Doc Haggerty
- Slim Jim, owner of the Denison saloon
- Little Jake
- Twink
- Red Scalp
- Pedro
- Fernando

TWIZZLE CHARACTERS

- Twizzle
- Footso the cat
- Chawky the white-faced golliwog
- Jiffy the broomstick man
- Polly Moppet
- Candy Floss, the mamma doll that can't say "mamma"
- Bouncy, the ball who has lost his bounce

7 Tiswas Teasers

Originating in the ATV region in the Midlands, Tiswas *eventually spread to become essential Saturday morning viewing for youngsters with latent anarchic tendencies, as well as with adults who didn't want to be old enough to know better. It was certainly an improvement on the BBC's rival* Multi-Coloured Swap Shop. *After all, who would want to swap Spit the Dog for Keith Chegwin? The phlegmatic Spit was one of the stars of* Tiswas, *even launching a range of T-shirts. Another favourite item was the cage in which kids were able to generally abuse grown-ups by covering them in soot or soaking them in water. Incredibly, there was a long queue from bank managers, estate agents, etc waiting to be subjected to this peculiar form of masochism.*

A1 What did Tiswas stand for?

A2 Which future star of *Three of a Kind* was a regular presenter on the show?

A3 What outrageous late night series did *Tiswas* spawn?

A4 And what did those letters stand for?

A5 Which mysterious cloaked figure specialised in hurling custard pies on *Tiswas*?

B6 Who conducted the show's 'almost legendary pop interviews'?

B7 Which former member of The Scaffold was a *Tiswas* presenter?

B8 Who was Spit the Dog's equally revolting feline playmate?

B9 Which *Tiswas* regular went on to become Dr Who?

B10 Which *Tiswas* mainstay later hosted *Everybody's Equal* and *Cluedo*?

C11 Who were the two original presenters of *Tiswas*?

C12 What were they known as?

C13 Which *Tiswas* presenter's father was Uncle Pat in *The Tingha and Tucker Club*?

C14 In a thirty week series, how many litres of shaving foam did *Tiswas* use?
a) 200 litres
b) 530 litres
c) 690 litres

C15 In a thirty week series, how many buckets of water did *Tiswas* get through?
a) 750
b) 900
c) 1350

CHILDREN'S HITMAKERS

☞ Father Abraham and the Smurfs
☞ The Archies
☞ The Chipmunks
☞ The Fraggles
☞ Keith Harris and Orville
☞ Kevin the Gerbil
☞ The Krankies
☞ The Monkees
☞ The Muppets
☞ The Partridge Family
☞ The Simpsons
☞ The Wombles

8   Pork Scratchings

Puppet pigs Pinky and Perky were so popular in the sixties that they received nearly as much fan mail as The Beatles. Fans used to send them all manner of creature comforts, including scarves, mittens, cardigans and cakes. And numerous guest stars popped in for a talk with pork, among them Michael Aspel, Freddie and the Dreamers and Henry Cooper.

A1   Who always wore the hat – Pinky or Perky?

A2   What was the name of their group which parodied The Fab Four?

A3   Who wore red – Pinky or Perky?

A4   What was Pinky and Perky's signature tune?

A5   What was the name of the show's resident bloodhound?

B6   Which Pinky and Perky presenter also starred as Det Sgt Stone in *Z Cars*?

B7   Who was the baby elephant who co-starred with Pinky and Perky?

B8   What was the name of the show's sultry female fox?

B9   Who was the Latin cow with distinctive long eyelashes?

B10   Which outsize comedy actor presented *Pinky and Perky*?

C11   After which year's Royal Variety Performance were Pinky and Perky presented to the royal family?
  a) 1963
  b) 1965
  c) 1967

C12 On which prestigious American TV programme did the porky pair make no fewer than six appearances?

C13 What was the name of the musical frog with Pinky and Perky?

C14 What was the pigs' own television company called?

C15 Who was Pinky and Perky's guest cat?

TORCHY CHARACTERS

- ☞ Torchy the Battery Boy
- ☞ Pom-Pom, the clockwork French poodle
- ☞ Flopsy, the rag doll
- ☞ Pilliwig, the toy clown
- ☞ Sparky, the baby dragon
- ☞ Squish, the space boy
- ☞ Pongo, the rag doll pirate
- ☞ King Dithers
- ☞ Bossy Boots

9   Blue Peter Crossword

Across

1 Surname of *Blue Peter*'s most famous female presenter. (9)

5 Intials of only *Blue Peter* presenter to return for a second spell. (1,1)

7 The infamous *Blue Peter* elephant – she made Val want to shout. (4)

8 Jack and Jill or Willow? (3)

9 See 1 down.

11 Donovan being catty? (5)

12 He just wouldn't get down from 19 across. (4)

15 Number of *Blue Peter* parrots. (3)

16 One of 6 down's puppies. (5)

19 Surname of the show's renowned daredevil presenter. (6)

20 Month of the year in which *Blue Peter* started in 1958 (abbreviation). (3)

21 First name of the hapless keeper in the saga of the *Blue Peter* elephant. (4)

23 Long-serving *Blue Peter* editor rarely landed in the soup. (6)

25 Some viewers thought Caron Keating wore the same clothes as this *Blue Peter* pony. (4)

26 First name of *Blue Peter* presenter who was hot stuff. (4)

Down

1 and 9 across There was only one type of plastic for Val. (6, 6)

2 and 22 down Ms Keating without transport (anagram). (2, 3)

3 *Blue Peter* would have been sunk without him. (5)

4 This presenter was a former trampoline champion

(surname). (6)
5 Presenter from 1967-79 (surname). (6)
6 The first *Blue Peter* dog. (5)
9 Parrot looking for an argument? (6)
10 3 down stood in for this film star on *Ben Hur* (surname). (6)
13 See 15 down.
14 *Blue Peter*'s sex-change tortoise. (5)
15 **and 13 down** She presented the show for a year from 1979. (4, 5)
17 Princess who joined Val on the 1971 safari to Kenya. (4)
18 The first (and sweetest?) *Blue Peter* guide dog. (5)
22 See 2 down.
24 Artist creator of Bengo the boxer puppy. (3)

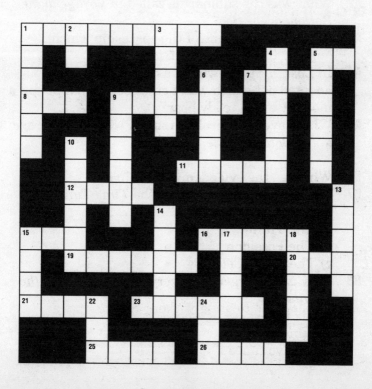

10   Land of Irwin Allen

Beginning with the TV spinoff from his 1961 movie Voyage
to the Bottom of the Sea, *Irwin Allen went on to complete a
quartet of cult sci-fi series in the sixties with* Lost in Space,
The Time Tunnel *and* Land of the Giants. *They were
masterpieces of special effects, but were made economically
viable by using the same stock footage over and over again.
This resulted in a definite sense of déja vu, particularly in
the course of the 110 episodes of* Voyage to the Bottom of the Sea
*where the underwater shot of the submarine was repeated
more times than* The African Queen.

A1   What was the name of the family who were *Lost
in Space*?

A2   What was the submarine called in *Voyage to the
Bottom of the Sea*?

A3   What was the name of the spaceship which
entered the *Land of the Giants*?

A4   In *Lost in Space*, what was the name of the
adopted pet which was a cross between a puppy, a
monkey and a teddy bear?

A5   Who played Admiral Harriman Nelson in *Voyage
to the Bottom of the Sea?*

B6   Who was the evil enemy agent in *Lost in Space*?

B7   On which doomed ship did the *Time Tunnel*
travellers first land?
a) The Titanic
b) The Poseidon
c) The Marie Celeste

B8   How much larger was everything in *Land of the
Giants*?
a) Six times
b) Nine times
c) Twelve times

B9 Who played Captain Lee Crane in *Voyage to the Bottom of the Sea*?

B10 Who were the two scientist heroes of *The Time Tunnel*?

C11 In what year was *Lost in Space* set?
a) 1997
b) 2001
c) 2020

C12 Who were the two leading actors in the film version of *Voyage to the Bottom of the Sea*?

C13 Who was the world's biggest detective in *Land of the Giants*?

C14 With which Western outlaw did the Time Tunnellers become involved?

C15 In *Lost in Space*, what was the name of the family's spaceship?

VOYAGE TO THE BOTTOM OF THE SEA CHARACTERS

☞ Admiral Harriman Nelson
☞ Captain Lee Crane
☞ Lt Commander Chip Morton
☞ Chief Sharkey
☞ Kowalski
☞ CPO Curley Jones
☞ Patterson
☞ Sparks
☞ Sonar

11 Smarter Than the Average Bear

A1 What is the name of the Flintstones' daughter?

A2 According to Dick Dastardly, what kind of hound is Muttley?

A3 What is *Boss Cat* known as in America?

A4 Which vegetable transforms Popeye into a he-man?

A5 At which National Park does Yogi Bear live?

B6 What kind of dog is Scooby Doo?

B7 Which cartoon scientist invented a means of travelling back through time?

B8 Who owns Precious Pup?

B9 Which custodian of the law is constantly outsmarted by Boss Cat and his gang?

B10 What kind of creature is Yakky Doodle?

C11 Who is the father in *The Jetsons*?

C12 What is the family name of the Hillbilly Bears?

C13 Which cartoon squid is janitor of a sea aquarium?

C14 What kind of animal is Bullwinkle, star of *The Bullwinkle Show*?

C15 To what organisation do Fred Flintstone and Barney Rubble belong?

SCOOBY DOO CHARACTERS

- ☞ Scooby
- ☞ Shaggy
- ☞ Velma
- ☞ Daphne
- ☞ Fred

DOCTOR WHO ENEMY FORCES

Among the lesser-known tribes and villains who crossed the Doctor's path were:

- ☞ Urbankans
- ☞ Plasmatons
- ☞ Ogrons
- ☞ Gundans
- ☞ Mechanoids
- ☞ Voords
- ☞ Zygons
- ☞ Sil
- ☞ The Kandyman
- ☞ Sontarans
- ☞ Drashigs
- ☞ The Krynoid
- ☞ The Rutan
- ☞ The Kroll

12   Who's Assistants

A1 Which of Dr Who's assistants was played by Frazer Hines?

A2 Which Dr Who had an assistant called Mel?

A3 And who played her?

A4 What was the name of the doggie robot in *Dr Who*?

A5 What was the name of the Brigadier who formed the task force UNIT?

B6 Who played Leela?

B7 Which *Blue Peter* stalwart played Steven Taylor?

B8 What was Zoe's surname?

B9 The fifth Doctor had an Australian assistant. What was her name?

B10 What was Perpugillian Brown better known as?

C11 Who played Vicki?

C12 Who was the third Doctor's first female assistant?

C13 Which female assistant made her debut in *The Evil of the Daleks*?

C14 Who played Adric?

C15 In which adventure did Romana first appear?

13   Connections

A1   What is the connection between Muffin the Mule and *Ryan's Daughter*?

A2   What is the connection between the Flowerpot Men and the Daleks?

A3   What is the connection between the gardener in *The Herbs* and *London's Burning*?

A4   What is the connection between Basil Brush and *The Likely Lads*?

A5   What is the connection between *Dr Who* and *Sir Lancelot*?

B6   What is the connection between Billy Bunter and Frank Spencer?

B7   What is the connection between *The Partridge Family* and *LA Law*?

B8   What is the connection between Bingo in *The Banana Splits* and *Huckleberry Hound*?

B9   What is the connection between *Rainbow* and *Z Cars*?

B10   What is the connection between Captain Scarlet and Paul Temple?

C11   What is the connection between *Junior Criss Cross Quiz* and The Sex Pistols?

C12   What is the connection between *Magpie* and the first edition of *Juke Box Jury*?

C13   What is the connection between The Monkees and Ena Sharples?

C14   What is the connection between Lenny the Lion and David Bowie?

C15   What is the connection between Jacques Tati and Ollie Beak?

14   Hi-Yo Silver!

Western heroes were always so virtuous. Hopalong Cassidy had his own code of conduct for youngsters, while the Lone Ranger embodied so much that was good and decent about America that he was invited to meet the President...Richard Nixon. But not everyone approved of these fearless frontiersmen. For example, the Brotherhood of Railroad Engineers flatly refused to endorse Casey Jones *simply because Alan Hale Jnr, who played Casey, was forced by cramped studio space to mount his engine cabin from the wrong side!*

A1   Who played the Lone Ranger?

A2   Who was the Cisco Kid's partner?

A3   What was the name of the last of the Mohicans?

A4   Who was 'king of the wild frontier'?

A5   Which Indian term, meaning 'faithful friend', did Tonto call the Lone Ranger?

B6   Who played Hopalong Cassidy?

B7   What was the name of the masked master swordsman played by Guy Williams?

B8   What was *The Range Rider*'s signature tune?

B9   Who played Davy Crockett?

B10   What colour did Hopalong Cassidy always wear?

C11   At what sport was Jay Silverheels, alias Tonto, once a professional?

C12   Who played Wild Bill Hickok?

C13   What was the Lone Ranger's real name?

C14   At what ranch was Gene Autry based?

C15   Who played Annie Oakley?

15   Human Partners

Can you work out the following human partners from their initials?

A1   Basil Brush: D. F.
A2   Tingha and Tucker: J.M.
A3   The Diddymen: K.D.
A4   Potty Time: M.B.
A5   Pussy Cat Willum: M.Y.

B6   Mikki the Martian: R.A.
B7   Theodore Rabbit: L.P.
B8   Archie Andrews: P.B.
B9   Mr Ed: W.P.
B10 Champion the Wonder Horse: R.N.

C11 Snoozy the sea-lion: D.S.
C12 Daisy May: S.
C13 Prudence Kitten: M.B.
C14 Flicka: K.M.
C15 Mr Turnip: H.L.

16   Superheroes

Even superheroes have their bad days. Take poor George Reeves, who played Superman on TV in the fifties. He became so associated with Superman that his appearance in a minor role in the film From Here to Eternity *was greeted with howls by a preview audience, after which the movie's producers decided to cut his part altogether. Finding himself well and truly typecast, Reeves was forced to find work as a wrestler until, in 1959, it all became too much for him and he shot himself. It seemed that Superman could do everything except get a job.*

A1   What is Superman's real name?
A2   Who played Batman on TV?
A3   Who is Marvel Comics' web spinning superhero?
A4   What is Batman's real name?
A5   And what is the name of his butler?

B6   Who is Marine Boy's father?
B7   From which planet does Superman come?
B8   Who is Gotham City's Chief of Police?
B9   What is Spiderman's real name?
B10 Buster ___ was one of the first actors to play Flash Gordon.

C11 Who is Marine Boy's mermaid companion?
C12 Who played Jimmy Olsen in the fifties TV version of *Superman*?
C13 Who narrated the *Batman* TV series?
C14 Near which fictional American town did Superman crashland on his arrival on Earth?
C15 Marine Boy's father was the leader of which organisation?

AMAZING HOLY BAT PHRASES

☞ "Holy Astringent Pomite Fruit."
☞ "Holy Contributing to the Delinquency of Minors."
☞ "Holy Fork in the Road."
☞ "Holy Hole in a Doughnut."
☞ "Holy Known-Unknown Flying Objects."
☞ "Holy Priceless Collection of Etruscan Snoods."
☞ "Holy Uncanny Photographic Mental Processes."

CLANGERS CHARACTERS

☞ Major Clanger
☞ Mother Clanger
☞ Small Clanger
☞ Tiny Clanger
☞ Grannie Clanger
☞ The two uncles, Brass Clanger and Copper Clanger
☞ The Soup Dragon
☞ Iron Chicken

17   Izzy Whizzy, Let's Get Busy!

Purchased for 7s 6d by engineer and part-time magician Harry Corbett during a wet family holiday in Blackpool in 1948, Sooty this year celebrates forty years in television. It has been a glorious career and the little bear hasn't aged a bit. You can't accuse him of having a neck like a turkey. This is in spite of the odd controversy which has seen him accused of introducing sex into children's television, pushing drugs, being too violent and being anti-police. He has even been kidnapped. Yes, it's a tough life being a glove puppet.

A1   What is Sooty's favourite musical instrument?

A2   Who is Sooty's canine partner in crime?

A3   What is the name of Sooty's magic dust?

A4   The introduction of which character resulted in BBC protests about bringing sex into children's TV?

A5   What is the name of Sooty's house?

B6   Which Yorkshire snake was introduced in the sixties?

B7   Which Liverpool pop star was taken to hospital after being knocked out on *The Sooty Show* in the early seventies?

B8   Which food product did Sooty advertise in the fifties?

B9   What was the name of *The Sooty Show*'s dozy cat?

B10   For how much did Harry Corbett insure the thumb and first two fingers of his right hand in the fifties?
  a) £3,000
  b) £8,000
  c) £20,000

C11 On which series did Sooty make his children's TV debut?

C12 Which *Carry On* star appeared in that series?

C13 Which regular *What's My Line* panelist was "hideously embarrassed" at meeting Sooty?

C14 Why was Sooty's little balsa-wood hammer banned in the fifties?

C15 Which rock group regularly featured Sooty in their concerts?
a) The Dooleys
b) The Boomtown Rats
c) Iron Maiden

VICTIMS OF SOOTY'S WATER PISTOL

They have included:

☞ Prince Philip
☞ George Harrison
☞ Jerry Hall
☞ Terry Wogan
☞ Russell Harty
☞ Barbara Woodhouse
☞ Gerry Marsden

18   Hosts with the Most

A1 Who was the first female presenter of *Blue Peter*?
A2 Who presented *Clapperboard*?
A3 Who was the main presenter of *Zoo Time*?
A4 Who presented *Stubby's Silver Star Show*?
A5 Who presented *How!*?

B6 Who presented *Little Big Time*?
B7 Who presented *Seeing Sport*?
B8 Who presented *Sketch Club*?
B9 Who presented *Junior Showtime*?
B10 Which former England centre-half presented *Junior Sportsview*?

C11 Who was the first presenter of *Lucky Dip*?
C12 Who presented *Whistle Stop*?
C13 Who presented *Top Score*?
C14 Who presented *Film Club*?
C15 Who presented *News from the Zoos*?

19   Pieces of Eight

A1 What was the name of Captain Pugwash's ship?

A2 Who played the hero in *The Buccaneers*?

A3 And what was the hero's name?

A4 Which famous pirate was played by Robert Newton?

A5 Who was Captain Pugwash's resourceful cabin boy?

B6 Who played Sir Francis Drake?

B7 Who was number 3's friendly rival?

B8 What was the name of the fishy seafarer in *Tintin*?

B9 Who was Captain Pugwash's arch rival?

B10 What was number 3's ship called?

C11 Who played Jim Hawkins in number 4?

C12 Which fifties series starred Lorne Greene as Captain Grant Mitchell?

C13 Who played Queen Elizabeth I in *Sir Francis Drake*?

C14 What was the name of the young stowaway who joined the crew of *The Buccaneers*?

C15 Who were the Buccaneers' sworn enemies?

20   Name the Year

Can you identify the following ten years from the clues?
Absolutely no marks will be given for being only a year out.

C1   John F. Kennedy was elected US President.
Prince Andrew was born.
New series included *Tales of the Riverbank* and
Ivor the Engine.

C2   ITV began transmission.
James Dean was killed.
New series included *The Woodentops*,
Crackerjack and *The Adventures of Robin Hood*.

C3   Neil Armstrong became the first man to land on
the moon.
Rolf Harris had a hit with 'Two Little Boys'.
Star Trek was first shown in Britain.

C4   The first Bond film, *Dr No*, was released.
The Telstar satellite was launched.
New series included *Animal Magic*, *Top of the
Form* and *Steptoe and Son*.

C5   Lord Lucan disappeared.
Abba won the Eurovision Song Contest with
'Waterloo'.
New series included *Bagpuss*, *Porridge* and *It
Ain't Half Hot Mum*.

C6   The year of the Munich air crash.
Elvis Presley was called up for military service.
New series included *Blue Peter*, *Ivanhoe* and
Oh Boy!

C7   The Beatles released *Sergeant Pepper*.
The BBC introduced Radio 1.
New series included *Captain Scarlet and the
Mysterons*, *Trumpton* and *The Prisoner*.

C8 King George VI died.

Singin' in the Rain was released.

New TV heroes included the Flowerpot Men and Billy Bunter.

C9 Sir Clive Sinclair introduced the first pocket calculator.

Little Jimmy Osmond threatened to be your 'Long-Haired Lover from Liverpool'.

New series included *Rainbow*, *Arthur of the Britons* and *Emmerdale Farm*.

C10 *The Sun* newspaper was launched.

Magistrates ordered the seizure of copies of the book *Fanny Hill*.

New series included *Pogle's Wood*, *Play School* and *Stingray*.

DO NOT ADJUST YOUR SET CAST

- ☞ Michael Palin
- ☞ Terry Jones
- ☞ Eric Idle
- ☞ David Jason
- ☞ Denise Coffey
- ☞ The Bonzo Dog Doo-Dah Band

21 Educationally Speaking

One of the first educational programmes on television was
All Your Own, which started on BBC in 1954. It encouraged
youngsters to show off their skills, whether it was model-
making or music-making. Among the budding musicians
were young classical guitarist John Williams, the King
Brothers, who enjoyed a few hits in the sixties, and a polite
fourteen year-old boy guitarist who gave his name as 'James
Page'. He later became Jimmy Page of Led Zeppelin.

A1 Who was the first presenter of *Newsround*?

A2 Which award winning programme for deaf
children succeeded the inspiringly titled *For Deaf
Children*?

A3 Who presented *Take Hart*?

A4 Who was the rustic panellist on *How!*?

A5 Which presenter, who later hosted *Winner Takes
All*, introduced *Top of the Form*?

B6 Which famous footballer was a presenter of
Junior Criss Cross Quiz?

B7 Who encouraged viewers to Do It Yourself on the
magazine programme *Focus*?

B8 What was the name of the BBC's long running
show for railway enthusiasts?

B9 Who talked about pets on *Tuesday Rendezvous*?

B10 Who was the 'Jim' in *The House That Jim Built*?

C11 Who devised the questions on *How!*?

C12 Who was the Australian question master in
Transworld Top Team?

C13 Which former ITN newsreader presented *You'd
Never Believe It*?

C14 What was the name of the robot space dog which joined John Earle and Jeremy Carrad in *Treasure House*?

C15 In the 1960s, which former rugby international presented *Hobbyhorse*?

THE JETSONS' GADGETS

- ☞ Nuclear-powered airmobile (with a side-saucer for the dog)
- ☞ Seeing-eye vacuum cleaner
- ☞ Videophone
- ☞ Voice-operated washing machine
- ☞ Solar-powered stamplicker
- ☞ The Foodarackacycle
- ☞ The Supersonic Dressomatic
- ☞ Push-button cook

TRUMPTON CHARACTERS

- ☞ Captain Flack
- ☞ Pugh, Pugh, Barney McGrew, Guthbert, Dibble and Grubb
- ☞ The Mayor
- ☞ Philby (the Mayor's chauffeur)
- ☞ Mr Troop the town clerk
- ☞ Sir Rufus and Lady de Trompe
- ☞ Mrs Cobbit the flowerseller
- ☞ Miss Lovelace from the hat shop (her dogs were Mitzi, Daphne and Lulu)
- ☞ Mr Munnings the printer
- ☞ Mr Craddock the park-keeper
- ☞ Mr Clamp the greengrocer
- ☞ Mr Platt the clockmaker
- ☞ Chippy Minton the carpenter, Mrs Minton and Nibs Minton (their son)
- ☞ Mr Antonio the ice-cream man
- ☞ Nick Fisher the bill poster
- ☞ Mr Wilkins the plumber
- ☞ Mr Robinson the window cleaner
- ☞ Raggy Dan the rag and bone man
- ☞ Walter Harking the painter
- ☞ Mr Wantage and Fred the telephone engineers

22   Monster Mash

A1 Who was the Addams Family's butler?

A2 Who was the (flat) head of the Munster household?

A3 Who was the only normal-looking member of the Munsters?

A4 Who played Grandpa in *The Munsters*?

A5 What was the name of Gomez's wife in *The Addams Family*?

B6 At what address did the Munsters live?

B7 Which veteran actor played Uncle Fester in *The Addams Family*?

B8 What was Gomez Addams' job?

B9 What creature could Grandpa Munster change into?

B10 In which comedy police series had *The Munsters'* Fred Gwynne previously starred with the actor from number 4?

C11 What was the name of Wednesday Addams' pet black widow spider?

C12 For which firm did number 2 work?

C13 What musical instrument did number 1 play?

C14 Who played Eddie Munster?

C15 How old was Grandpa Munster?
   a) 256
   b) 378
   c) 490

23 Watch With Mother Crossword

Across

1 The Woodentops' major source of milk. (9)

5 Is the Flowerpot Men's home made of this? (4)

7 and 17 across Voice of the Flowerpot Men. (5, 7)

9 Speed of the tortoise coach in *The Flowerpot Men*. (4)

11 Surname of the first *Picture Book* reader. (8)

12 and 10 down She always came between Bill and Ben. (6, 4)

15 and 24 across The tales she could tell about being in that basket all week. (5, 3)

16 It was a feather in Maria's cap to be storyteller on *Andy Pandy*. (4)

17 See 7 across.

21 and 14 down The star of Tuesday's edition of *Watch With Mother*. (4, 5)

24 See 15 across.

25 The Woodentops' twin girl. (5)

26 Day of *The Flowerpot Men* (abbreviation). (3)

Down

1 The rabbit in Thursday's *Watch With Mother*. (7)

2 ... and the mouse. (3)

3 ... and the hedgehog. (3)

4 Monday's *Watch With Mother* programme. (7, 4)

5 Restrains part of the work of the Woodentops' cleaning lady. (5)

6 Or was it Ben? (4)

8 and 22 down Canine hero of *The Woodentops*. (6, 3)

10 See 12 across.

13 Andy's furry friend. (5)

14 See 21 across.
16 Andy's residence. (6)
18 The Woodentops' boy twin. (5)
19 The Woodentops' farm-hand. (3)
20 '___ to go home'. (4)
22 See 8 down.
23 Type of animal of 1 across. (3)

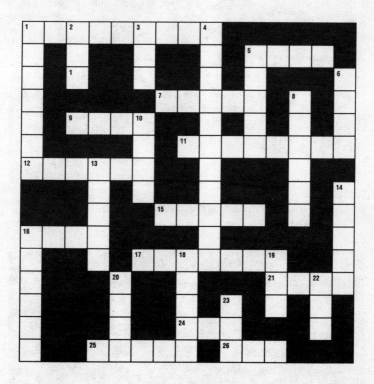

Picture Quiz
Number One

B1 In *Thunderbirds*, what was the name of Kyrano's daughter?

B2 What happened next?

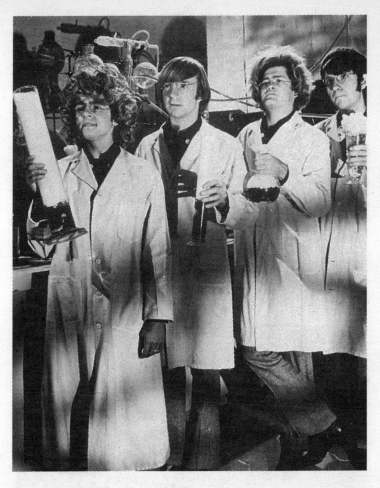

B3 What did some American stations initially object to about The Monkees?

B4 Which game is in progress and on which show?

B5 Which actor, cunningly disguised as Captain Bird's Eye, is pictured with Pinky and Perky?

B6 Which underwater action series is this?

B7 Which creatures are these?

B8 Which series is pictured here?

The Fifties

You never knew what you might stumble across on children's television in the fifties. At 4.45pm one afternoon in 1955, the BBC presented a programme called Popie *(not to be confused with Olive Oyl's pal) in which, according to the* Radio Times *of the day, 'W. Macqueen-Pope, theatre historian, continues his stories of gay London nights.' Ooooer! It was, of course, all perfectly innocent and no indication of any future moral decline at the BBC. So there was no danger of* Lady Chatterley's Lover *being featured on* Jackanory, Sketch Club *coming live from a strip joint in Soho or Val showing us how to make a G-string out of an elastic band and some milk bottle tops.*

A1 Who were the pear-shaped creatures from the planet Bumble?

A2 And who created them?

A3 What was Billy Bunter's nickname?

A4 Who played Mr Pastry?

A5 Which comedy duo was played by Charlie Drake and Jack Edwardes?

A6 What did Roger Moore, alias Ivanhoe, used to model?

A7 What was the cuckoo called on *Billy Bean and His Funny Machine*?

A8 Which series featured Larry the Lamb and Dennis the Dachshund?

A9 Who played Hawkeye in *Hawkeye and the Last of the Mohicans*?

A10 Who was Roy Rogers' wife?

A11 What was Monkee Mickey Dolenz known as when he starred in *Circus Boy*?

A12 What was the name of the flying squirrel in *The Bullwinkle Show*?

B13 Who starred as Jim Hardie in *The Tales of Wells Fargo*?

B14 Which talent-spotter presented his *Junior Discoveries*?

B15 Which husband and wife team contributed happy cooking to *Lucky Dip*?

B16 Which Enid Blyton hero was a mainstay of early children's ITV?

B17 In which continent was *Jungle Boy* set?

B18 Who created Hank the cowboy?

B19 Who was Billy Bunter's odious form master?

B20 Sooty's early shows were called *Magic and* ___.
a) *Mayhem*
b) *Mischief*
c) *Sausages*

B21 Which children's drama serial centred around an 'ordinary, workaday family living in a little house'?

B22 Who was the circus boss in *Circus Boy*?

B23 What was the name of Roy Rogers' dog?

B24 Who owned Fury?

B25 Who was the resident pianist on *Whirligig*?

C26 Which associate of Robin Hood used to be in *Mrs Dale's Diary*?

C27 Which series told the adventures of a pit pony?

C28 Who presented *A to Zoo*?

C29 Who had a drawing board called Willoughby which used to come to life?

C30 Which father of a *Magpie* presenter introduced *Animal Alphabet*?

C31 What character was Dr Bill Baxter better known as?

C32 And which singing cowboy played him?

C33 Which future star of *Man About the House* played Little Lord Fauntleroy in 1957?

C34 Who played Tugboat Annie?

C35 And who was Annie's great rival?

C36 Who introduced *Playbox*?

C37 Who performed magic on *Whirligig*?

C38 What was the name of the hare with Pinky and Perky?

C39 Which telescope was an early children's TV star?

C40 What kind of vehicles featured in *Colonel Crock*?

SUPERCAR CHARACTERS

- ☞ Mike Mercury
- ☞ Doctor Beaker
- ☞ Mitch the Monkey
- ☞ Professor Popkiss
- ☞ Masterspy
- ☞ Zarin
- ☞ Jimmy Gibson

FIREBALL XL5 CHARACTERS

- ☞ Steve Zodiac
- ☞ Professor Matic
- ☞ Lieutenant Ninety
- ☞ Zoonie
- ☞ Venus
- ☞ Robert the Robot
- ☞ Commander Zero

Batbusters

Executive producer William Dozier knew exactly what he was doing when planning the great Batman series of the sixties. "I had the simple idea of overdoing it, of making it so square and so serious that adults would find it amusing. I knew kids would go for the derring-do, the adventure." But his format raised a few eyebrows in high places. Dozier says: "I explained to ABC executives how we were going to do it – that we were going to have 'ZAP' and 'POW'. And ABC president Leonard Goldenson said, 'We are going to have, right on the screen, 'ZAP' and 'POW'?' I said, 'Yeah, and a lot more, Leonard.' 'Oh my,' he said."

A1   What H was the name of Bruce Wayne's aunt?
A2   What R played the Joker?
A3   What N played Alfred?
A4   What G is the city in which *Batman* is set?
A5   What D is Robin's real name?

B6   What S was played by Joan Collins?
B7   What R played Chief O'Hara?
B8   What G played the Riddler?
B9   What B was Batgirl's real name?
B10   What P was played by Burgess Meredith?

C11   What H was first choice to play Batman?
C12   What L played Dr Cassandra?
C13   What M was the Batvillain who strummed a lute?
C14   What P was played by Maurice Evans?
C15   What C was Fingers otherwise known as?

27   First Names

A number of characters are suffering an identity crisis. Put them out of their misery by filling in the names.

B1 ___ Wombat (*The Tingha and Tucker Club*).
B2 ___ Pitstop (*Wacky Races*).
B3 ___ the Mouse (his own fifties animation series).
B4 ___ Mole (*Barnaby*).
B5 ___ the dog (*The Herbs*).
B6 ___ the toad (*Bagpuss*).
B7 ___ McGrew (*Trumpton*).
B8 ___ the hippopotamus (*Rainbow*).
B9 ___ Gibson (*Supercar*).
B10 ___ the Venusian (*Space Patrol*).
B11 ___ the camel (*Telescope*).
B12 ___ Bloodnok (*The Telegoons*).
B13 ___ Brady (*The Roy Rogers Show*).
B14 ___ Nelson (*Sea Hunt*).
B15 ___ McKeever (*Ripcord*).
B16 ___ Randall (*Timeslip*).
B17 ___ Rand (*Star Trek*).
B18 ___ Nugent (*Billy Bunter*).
B19 ___ Frog (*Hector's House*).
B20 ___ the Bad (*Noggin the Nog*).

Who's Who

A1 Who asked youngsters to "keep 'em peeled" on *Junior Police 5*?

A2 Who has presented *Record Breakers* throughout its twenty year run?

A3 Who started to Fix It in 1975?

A4 Who sang 'Come Outside' with Wendy Richard and presented *Junior Criss Cross Quiz*?

A5 Who was the Hot Chestnut Man?

B6 Who narrated the stories of Bengo?

B7 Who gave gardening tips on *Focus* and later looked after the *Blue Peter* garden?

B8 Who was the female presenter of *Vision On*?

B9 Who played Jimmy in *H.R. Pufnstuf*?

B10 Who presented *Origami*?

C11 Who narrated *Joe*?

C12 Who sang the *Stingray* theme?

C13 Who appeared with Buddy Budgerigar?

C14 Who presented *Colonel Crock*?

C15 Who was in *Jumbleland*?

Famous Settings

Below are fifteen children's series and fifteen locations, all jumbled up. Can you match them up correctly?

B1	*Hopalong Cassidy*	New Providence
B2	*Noddy*	Wameru Study Centre
B3	*Pingwings*	Hooterville
B4	*F Troop*	Nut Wood
B5	*Rupert*	The Bar 20
B6	*Petticoat Junction*	Berrydown Farm
B7	*Superman*	Toyland
B8	*The Tomorrow People*	Fort Apache
B9	*Twizzle*	Metropolis
B10	*Stingray*	Space City
B11	*The Buccaneers*	Stray Town
B12	*The Adventures of William Tell*	Fort Courage
B13	*Daktari*	The Lab
B14	*Fireball XL5*	Altdorf
B15	*Rin Tin Tin*	Marineville

A1 Which of the following was not in *Daktari*?
a) Clarence the cross-eyed lion
b) Judy the chimp
c) Gerald the giraffe

A2 Which of the following was not in *Do Not Adjust Your Set*?
a) Eric Idle
b) John Cleese
c) Michael Palin

A3 Which of the following did not play Darrin in *Bewitched*?
a) Dick Van Dyke
b) Dick Sargent
c) Dick York

A4 Which of the following was not in *Noggin the Nog*?
a) Thor Nogson
b) Olaf the Lofty
c) Thrednog the Thin

A5 Which of the following did not present *Junior Criss Cross Quiz*?
a) Jeremy Hawk
b) Bob Holness
c) Reg Varney

B6 Which of the following was not a member of the *How!* panel?
a) Bunty James
b) Jon Miller
c) Sally James

B7 Which of the following was not one of *The Herbs*?
a) Sage the owl
b) Thyme the clockmender
c) Dill the dog

B8 Which of the following was not in *Camberwick Green*?
a) Mr Sheen
b) Dr Mopp
c) Windy Miller

B9 Which of the following was not in *Pipkins*?
a) Topov the monkey
b) Harry the horse
c) Pig

B10 Which of the following was not an agent in *Captain Scarlet and the Mysterons*?
a) Captain Cerise
b) Captain Ochre
c) Captain Magenta

C11 Which of the following was not a guest on *The Adventures of Robin Hood*?
a) Leo McKern
b) Claire Rayner
c) Thora Hird

C12 Which of the following was not a member of Scooby Doo's gang?
a) Shaggy
b) Floppy
c) Freddy

C13 Which of the following was not one of the Brady Bunch?
a) Steve
b) Greg
c) Bobby

C14 Which of the following did not present *Tom Tom*?
a) Jeremy Carrad
b) Jeremy Paxman
c) John Earle

31 Boom! Boom!

Basil Brush is the most famous fox in the world. His tales have been translated into such diverse tongues as Afrikaans and Japanese and he is even a star in Germany, where he is known as Balduin Schwupp. The Americans weren't so sure, however. They didn't take the TV series and wanted to change the character's name in the books, because they didn't think the name Basil sounded sufficiently macho. I bet they didn't have the guts to tell him that, face to snout.

A1 Who supplies the voice of Basil Brush?

A2 On which British comedy actor was the voice based?

A3 Which of Basil's straight men also presented *Get It Together*?

A4 Complete the end-of-show song title: '___ Off Basil'.

A5 Which of Basil's human partners went on to star in *Yes, Minister*?

B6 Who created Basil?

B7 On which show did Basil make his début?

B8 One of his accomplices on that show was Spike ___?

B9 What type of creature was he?

B10 Which of Basil's stooges starred in the sitcom *Dear Mother...Love Albert*?

C11 With which famous TV magician did Basil appear in the mid-sixties?

C12 When did Basil get his own series?
   a) 1968
   b) 1970
   c) 1974

C13 Number 1 also used to play a policeman in a whodunnit sequence in *Playbox*. What was the policeman's name?

C14 Which of Basil's straight men appeared in the ill-fated ITV series *The Bretts*?

C15 Which human foil to Basil once presented a fifties children's information programme called *Enquiry Unlimited* with Redvers Kyle?

EARLY CRACKERJACK GIRLS

☞ Frances Barlow
☞ Jillian Comber
☞ Pip Hinton
☞ Christine Holmes
☞ Vivienne Martin
☞ Valerie Walsh

32   Early Breaks

Children's television has been a breeding ground for many future stars. How many of the following can you recognise?

A1 Which comedy actor graduated from *Do Not Adjust Your Set* to Nelson Mandela House?

A2 Which British actress co-starred with Skippy?

A3 Which landlady of the Queen Vic once presented *Play Away*?

A4 Which teen idol starred in *The Partridge Family*?

A5 Which actor played a knight before becoming James Bond?

B6 Which rock legend demonstrated canoeing and rock climbing as a teenager on *Seeing Sport*?

B7 Which Hollywood star once played a convict in an episode of *The Adventures of William Tell*?

B8 Who progressed from reading stories on *Rainbow* to starring in *Tenko* and *The Colbys*?

B9 Who played one of Billy Bunter's chums before starring in *Blow Up*?

B10 Who exchanged *Play Away* for *Brideshead Revisited*?

C11 Which theatrical Dame was a storyteller on *Rainbow*?

C12 Who avoided being a prisoner when playing Sir Glavin in an episode of *The Adventures of Sir Lancelot*?

C13 Which British comedy actor, renowned for dropping his trousers on screen, played Wat Longfellow in *The Adventures of Robin Hood*?

C14 Which star of *The Rocky Horror Show* played a humble cashier in *Ace of Wands*?

Movie Clips

A1 Who played Superman in the series of box office hits starting in 1978?

A2 Who played the Joker in the 1989 film *Batman*?

A3 Which legendary character starred in *Sword of Sherwood Forest*?

A4 What was the title of the first *Thunderbirds* movie?

A5 Which popular sixties children's series do you associate with the film *Dougal and the Blue Cat*?

B6 Which movie led to the TV series *Daktari*?

B7 Which *Rising Damp* star appeared in *Wombling Free*?

B8 Which city did the Muppets take in 1984?

B9 Complete the title: *The Lone Ranger and the Lost* ___.

B10 When was the first *Star Trek* movie released?
a) 1977
b) 1978
c) 1979

C11 What part of the anatomy was the title of a Monkees film?

C12 Which horror movie actor and small screen Sherlock Holmes starred in *Dr Who and the Daleks*?

C13 Which future movie queen was a child actress in the 1943 film *Lassie Come Home*?

C14 In what year did the Lone Ranger first appear on film?
a) 1933
b) 1938
c) 1944

C15 Who played Superman in two forties film serials?

34   Catchphrases

A1   Who says: "Yus, M'Lady"?

A2   Who asks: "You rannnnng"?

A3   Who shouts: "Yabba dabba doo"?

A4   At the end of which show would we be told: "The worst is yet to come"?

A5   Which programme always started with: "It's a bird...it's a plane..."?

B6   Who used to say: "Hullo, Auntie Jean"?

B7   In what show would you hear: "Hey, Drooper, take out the trash"?

B8   Who used to enthuse: "Goody, goody gumdrops"?

B9   Whose catchphrase was "Heavens to Murgatroyd"?

B10   Whose exclamations included "Yarooh", "Crikey" and "Beast"?

C11   Which harassed crook used to suggest "Plan X"?

C12   Who finished each show with: "Whatever else it will be, it will be well and truly...all your own"?

C13   Who used to sign off: "And don't forget, look after dear old mum"?

C14   Whose catchphrase was: "Don't embawass me"?

C15   Whose parting words were always: "Adios amigos"?

35 Play School Presenters Wordsearch

Find the sixteen Play School presenters (surnames only) and three toys hidden in the square window. Beware: some are diagonal and in reverse.

```
A D I E M G R I F F I T H S W
I I D W U O E I N S T E I N L
R O A D N W B O V L I S F M N
C R O P R E J E M I M A G A O
D O G M O R T O N V T T H Y R
B I G T E D I M J J N R A A E
S T O A T U N A U C A U R L D
T M H T H C C J D H C M R L A
E I S O O K J O G E E P I T E
V N T G M O O S E L E N S N L
E O I A J P U L L L L A B O P
N G N Z O A S H C R O F T O Z
S U G Z N T T O S B O U R N E
V E G A E H L I N E K E R E B
Y A T E S L I T T L E T E D U
```

36   Creative Talents

A1   Who created *Torchy?*
A2   Who created *Captain Pugwash*?
A3   Who created *The Flintstones*?
A4   Who created *Star Trek*?
A5   Who created Batman?

B6   Who created Billy Bunter?
B7   Who created *Sir Prancelot*?
B8   Who created The Addams Family?
B9   Who created *The Herbs*?
B10 Who created *The Clangers*?

C11 Who created the Lone Ranger?
C12 Who created Superman?
C13 Who created *Catweazle*?
C14 Who created Little Grey Rabbit?
C15 Who created *Blue Peter*?
C16 Who created *Tales of the Riverbank*?
C17 Who created *Space Patrol*?
C18 Who created *Crystal Tipps and Alistair*?
C19 Which company created *Mr Benn*?
C20 Who created *The Tomorrow People*?

37   Children's Drama

A1 Who played Orlando?
A2 From which adult series was it a spin-off?
A3 Which *Bergerac* regular appeared in *The Adventures of Garry Halliday*?
A4 Who starred as White Hunter?
A5 Who was Garry Halliday's arch enemy?

B6 Who played Sexton Blake?
B7 Which gang of crime-fighting teenagers (not modelled on Del Boy's means of transport) included Mike, Jill, Steve, Dave and Sue?
B8 Who played Francis Storm?
B9 Which newspaper was run by Peter, Andy, Tubby, Swot and 'Fred'?

C10 Complete the titles.
a) *The Flaxton* ___
b) *Tom Grattan's* ___
c) *The Splendid* ___
C11 Which series starred Graydon Gould as George Keeley?
C12 Which seemingly meek but intrepid hero was played by Wally Cox?
C13 What was Orlando's lucky charm called?
C14 What was the name of Sexton Blake's car?
C15 How many children did the Appleyards have?

38   Name the Show

Identify the children's TV programmes from the three clues given.

A1   A TV version of *The Goon Show*.
It was transmitted on Saturday teatime from 1963.
Characters included Eccles, Bluebottle and Neddy Seagoon.

A2   This pair were often assisted by Professor Billy McComb.
They comprised a naughty schoolboy and a duck.
Ray Alan had a hand in it somewhere.

A3   This programme first appeared in 1972.
It acknowledges outstanding achievements.
Every edition has been presented by Roy Castle.

B4   Richard Dimbleby used to introduce the radio version.
The television presenters included David Dimbleby and Paddy Feeny.
It was first screened in 1962.

B5   The successor to *Tuesday Rendezvous*.
Jimmy Hanley used to make models on this show.
Another regular contributor was Daisy the cow.

B6   Presenters included Stuart McGugan and Gordon Rollings.
It was created by Joy Whitby in 1964.
Among the regulars were Hamble and Humpty.

B7   They were small mouse-like creatures.
They lived on a blue moon.
They communicated by whistling.

C8 *Brookside* mentor Phil Redmond wrote some
episodes of this seventies drama.
It was created by Charlotte Mitchell.
The central family were the Gathercoles.

C9 One of the principal employers was a biscuit
factory.
The factory manager was Mr Cresswell.
The local farmer was Jonathan Bell.

C10 A period adventure first screened in 1962.
Roy Kinnear used to make guest appearances.
Dermot Walsh played the title role.

C11 Made by Yorkshire Television.
Stars included Arthur English.
A horsey tale.

C12 Part of the BBC's *Tales from Europe* in the
sixties.
Princess Thousandbeauty was a major character.
Her would-be suitor was turned into a bear.

TARGET LUNA – THE WEDGWOOD FAMILY

☞ Professor Wedgwood
☞ Mrs Wedgwood
☞ Valerie Wedgwood
☞ Geoffrey Wedgwood
☞ Jimmy Wedgwood

It's Friday, it's Five to Five...

Besides being terrific entertainment, Crackerjack *offered valuable exposure to the top pop acts of the day. Leslie Crowther remembers Tom Jones making only his second television appearance on* Crackerjack. *"He sang 'It's Not Unusual', but afterwards the producer was a bit worried about Tom's typical pelvic thrusts. So the next time we had Tom on, we decided to get him to perform something a bit more restrained. He chose 'The Skye Boat Song' and the producer thought it would be just right for a family audience. But there was no changing Tom and even the peaceful lyrics 'over the sea to Skye' were accompanied by a series of violent bodily thrusts. We had to shoot him from the waist up!"*

A1 Who was the first presenter of *Crackerjack*?

A2 What were the show's famous writing instruments?

A3 What was the name of the programme's game where contestants' arms were filled with prizes?

A4 And what did the contestants receive if they got an answer wrong?

A5 Which *Crackerjack* presenter was once a BBC newsreader?

B6 Which member of the *Crackerjack* team had been spare man to The Crazy Gang?

B7 Who was *Sorry* after being resident comic on *Crackerjack* in the fifties?

B8 Which *Crackerjack* host was also a regular on *The Black and White Minstrel Show*?

B9 Which *Crackerjack* presenter had been a Radio 1 disc jockey?

B10 And what was his nickname?

C11 Which of the *Crackerjack* girls used to introduce the BBC's teenage show *Gadzooks! It's All Happening* in 1965?

C12 Who were the first two resident comedians on *Crackerjack*?

C13 Who was the show's long-standing bandleader?

C14 Which *Crackerjack* girl later attempted to become a female Gary Glitter as pop singer Kristine Sparkle?

C15 Which *Crackerjack* compère was once sacked from his job with an insurance company for sneaking off to commentate on a soccer match?

THE PARTRIDGE FAMILY HITS

☞ I Think I Love You
☞ It's One of Those Nights (Yes Love)
☞ Breaking Up is Hard to Do
☞ Looking Through the Eyes of Love
☞ Walking in the Rain

In addition to the likes of Dr Who, Thunderbirds *and* Star Trek, *a number of other science fiction series crash-landed on to children's television during the Golden Age. The budgets for some of these were ridiculously small, with the result that the entire population of London was often supposed to be terrorised by nothing more menacing than a rubber glove or a monster taken from the inside of a cornflakes packet. But it didn't stop us cowering behind the sofa just in case...*

A1 Who played Catweazle?

A2 What was the name of the family in *Pathfinders in Space*?

A3 Who was the leader of *The Tomorrow People*?

A4 Who starred in *Planet of the Apes*?

A5 Who was the magical hero of *Ace of Wands*?

B6 Who was the farmer's son who befriended Catweazle?

B7 In which subterranean conurbation was *City Beneath the Sea* set?

B8 What was the name of the chimp played by number 4 in *Planet of the Apes*?

B9 What was the owl called in *Ace of Wands*?

B10 Which seventies pop group did Tomorrow Person Mike Holoway form?

C11 What was the name of the Midlands village where the young heroes of *Timeslip* first vanished?

C12 Who was the evil rebel scientist in *Phoenix Five*?

C13 Which gripping science fiction serial, following the adventures of young Ian Spencer, was a vital ingredient of *Whirligig* in the early fifties?

C14 What was the name of the campaigning science journalist played by Gerald Flood in *Plateau of Fear* and *City Beneath the Sea*?

C15 Who were the family in the 1956 BBC serial *Space School*?

PIPKINS CHARACTERS

☞ Hartley Hare
☞ Topov the Monkey
☞ Pig
☞ Tortoise
☞ Octavia the Ostrich
☞ Mrs Muddle

☞ The part of Mrs Muddle was played by Sue Nicholls, who is currently Audrey Roberts in *Coronation Street*. Recalling her days sharing the spotlight with Hartley, Sue says, "Playing next to a tatty hare was wonderful." We understand that Hartley's lawyers have been informed.

It's amazing what rock stars will do to promote their latest record on television. Nowadays, they sit in the Broom Cupboard on Children's BBC and pretend that they understand the repartee of a puppet duck. In the old days, it might have been a case of discussing the merits of that year's Blue Peter *advent candle with Val or performing a duet with Ollie Beak on* The Five O'Clock Club. *But everyone has to start somewhere. Back in the sixties on a children's TV series called* Pops and Lenny, The Beatles *were once the support act to Lenny the Lion!*

A1 Whose seventies pop series was titled *Shang-A-Lang*?
a) The Osmonds
b) The Bay City Rollers
c) Def Leppard

A2 What was The Monkees' first UK hit?
a) 'Last Train to Clarksville'
b) 'I'm a Believer'
c) 'Daydream Believer'

A3 What was Ayshea's surname?
a) Bough
b) Brough
c) Diamonds

A4 Which of the following did not appear on *Crackerjack*?
a) Roy Orbison
b) Cliff Richard
c) Elvis Presley

B5 Who was Roy North's co-presenter on *Get It Together*?
a) Meg Richardson
b) Megg Nicoll
c) Megs Jenkins

B6 Which Monkee had a solo hit with 'Rio'?
a) Davy Jones
b) Mike Nesmith
c) Peter Tork

B7 Which seventies teenybop group had their own children's TV series?
a) Arrows
b) Kenny
c) The New Seekers

B8 What were The Monkees originally called?
a) The Beach Boys
b) The Turtles
c) The Walker Brothers

C9 Which Animal presented *Monster Music Mash* in 1969?
a) Lenny the Lion
b) Basil Brush
c) Alan Price

C10 Who presented *Discotheque*?
a) Gerry Marsden
b) Billy J. Kramer
c) Robert Robinson

C11 Mickey Dolenz's father George starred in which adventure series?
a) *The Count of Monte Cristo*
b) *The Scarlet Pimpernel*
c) *Sword of Freedom*

C12 Who played Danny in *The Partridge Family*?
a) Danny Baker
b) Danny Bonaduce
c) Danny Blanchflower

42   To Boldly Go

Like so many cult series, Star Trek *was beset by teething troubles in the early stages. The American NBC network were particularly worried about some of the characters – they thought the sight of Spock would alienate viewers and they also feared the presence of a multi-racial crew might cause offence. In the end, the network succeeded where the Klingons had failed and the Starship* Enterprise's *mission was aborted after seventy-eight episodes. One thing always puzzled me: If Spock's mind was so ordered and logical, why didn't he point out that 'to boldly go' was a bad case of a split infinitive?*

A1   Spock was half-human, half-___?

A2   What was Chief Medical Officer Leonard McCoy better known as?

A3   What was Scotty's first name?

A4   What nationality was Mr Sulu?

A5   Who was the *Enterprise*'s Communications Officer?

B6   What did the 'T' stand for in Captain James T. Kirk?

B7   Which US President named a space shuttle *Enterprise* in honour of *Star Trek*?

B8   Who played Ensign Chekov?

B9   Which of the *Enterprise*'s enemies modelled themselves on the Roman army?

B10   What was the *Enterprise* originally going to be called?

C11   What race were so hideous that one look could drive a man insane?

C12   The *Enterprise*'s top speed was Warp Eight. How many times the speed of light was this?

C13   Who played Nurse Christine Chapel?

C14 What was James T. Kirk's name originally going to be?

C15 Who was the former commanding officer kidnapped by a mutinous Spock in the two-part story *The Menagerie*?

STAR TREK CATCHPHRASES

☞ "Beam me up, Scotty."
☞ "Captain's log, stardate…"
☞ "Highly illogical, Captain."
☞ "It's life, but not as we know it."
☞ "Klingons on the starboard bow."
☞ "Space, the final frontier."
☞ "To boldly go where no man has gone before."

SPACE PATROL CHARACTERS

☞ Captain Larry Dart
☞ Husky
☞ Slim
☞ Professor Haggerty
☞ Colonel Raeburn, base commander
☞ Marla, Raeburn's secretary
☞ Cassiopea, Haggerty's daughter
☞ Gabblerdictum, a Martian parrot

43   Cartoon Crossword

Across

1   Huckleberry Hound's favourite song. (10)
3   One of the Rugg family. (4)
5   The Flinstones' home town. (7)
8   The voice of Bugs Bunny, Daffy Duck and many others (surname). (5)
10   Snagglepuss was one such animal. (4)
11   Quick Draw McGraw was one of these. (5)
14   Surname of Fred Flintstone's boss. (5)
15   Space-age family. (7)
18   Hokey ___. (4)
19   Natural hue of the Panther. (4)
21   As in Fog and Leg. (4)
24   The world's most dynamic insect. (4, 3)
25   Deputy Dawg's ratty pal. (5)

Down

1   Repetitive member of Boss Cat's gang. (4, 4)
2   Mr Jinx hated them to pieces. (6)
4   Where the bears in 3 across might live. (4)
6   The apple of Popeye's eye (surname). (3)
7   Deputy Dawg's gopher. (5)
9   Doggie Daddy's offspring. (5)
12   Good job he missed tea at the start or this guy could have been a nuisance to Fred Flintstone. (6)
14   Jumpy member of TC's alley cats. (5)
16   Cowardly dog. (6)
17   Always on the ball to help TC. (5)
18   Fred Flintstone's 'er indoors. (5)
20   The Flintstones' family pet. (4)
22   Desperately seeking Jerry. (3)
23   He was precious to Granny Sweet. (3)

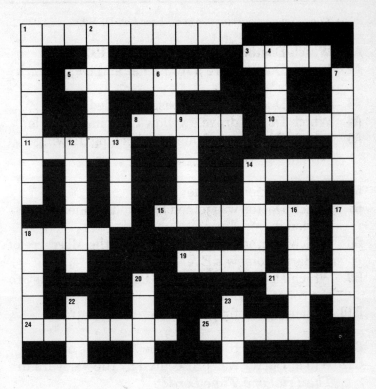

44   Which Doctors

The following questions are all based on Dr Who.

A1   Which Doctor was on screen from 1970-74?

A2   Which Doctor wore a funny hat and baggy check trousers?

A3   Which Doctor had an assistant called Polly?

A4   Which Doctor drove a yellow car named Bessie?

A5   Which Doctor was famed for his long, flowing scarf?

B6   Which Doctor first met K9?

B7   Which Doctor was joined by a young alien, Turlough?

B8   Which Doctor became involved in the Massacre of St Bartholomew's Eve?

B9   Which Doctor joined Marco Polo on his journey to the court of Kublai Khan?

B10   Which Doctor first encountered the Yeti?

C11   Which Doctor confronted the Androids of Tara?

C12   Which Doctor was prosecuted by the Valeyard in *The Trial of a Time Lord*?

C13   Which Doctor tangled with an insect race, the Wirrn, in *The Ark in Space*?

C14   Which Doctor fought for his freedom in *The Celestial Toymaker*?

C15   Which Doctor met the dastardly Professor Zaroff in the lost city of Atlantis in a story entitled *The Underwater Menace*?

45   **The Sixties**

A1 What was the name of the adventure serial on *The Banana Splits*?

A2 Who was the ferocious dog who joined *The Sooty Show* in the 1960s?

A3 Besides *Do Not Adjust Your Set*, in which other series did Captain Fantastic appear?

A4 What type of birds did the Pingwings resemble?

A5 Which renowned stargazer gave astronomy tips on *Focus*?

A6 What was the name of the cat in *Hector's House*?

A7 What was the name of the Italian mouse with big ears who was a great favourite on *Sunday Night at the London Palladium*?

A8 Which famous (indeed possibly only) exponent of the zither appeared on the inter-city quiz *Top Score*?

A9 Who played Maxwell Smart in *Get Smart*?

A10 What was the name of the Martian in *Space Patrol*?

A11 Which evil *Dr Who* character was responsible for creating the Daleks?

A12 Who was the undeniable star of *Tales of the Riverbank*?

B13 What was Orlando's surname?

B14 Who was the long-running scorer on *Top of the Form*?

B15 Which *Crackerjack* presenter was once an Ovaltiney?

B16 What did Marine Boy chew so that he could stay underwater without oxygen?

B17 What was the name of the rat in *Tales of the Riverbank*?

B18 Who narrated *Herge's Adventures of Tintin*?

B19 What was the surname of Dr Who's assistant Jamie?

B20 Who presented *Top Dogs*?

B21 What was the name of Marsh Tracy's daughter in *Daktari*?

B22 Who ran the Primrose Gap Trading Post in *F Troop*?

B23 From which country did *Cristobal and Company* originate?

B24 Who played Mrs Muir in *The Ghost and Mrs Muir*?

C25 What did WIN stand for in *Joe 90*?

C26 What was the name of the bird in *The Tingha and Tucker Club*?

C27 Which actor, who starred in *All Gas and Gaiters* and *Oh Brother!*, did some of the voices for *The Rubovian Legends*?

C28 Who presented Camera Club on *Focus*?

C29 Who played the Voice in *The Adventures of Garry Halliday*?

C30 Who were *The Impossibles*?

C31 Which British blues and R 'n' B mentor was the unlikely provider of the music on *Five O'Clock Funfair*?

C32 What was the full name of Dr Who's assistant Romana?

C33 Who was the Father of the Canadian North-West in *Tomahawk*?

C34 At which Air Force base was *No Time for Sergeants* set?

C35 Who were Kate Bradley's three daughters in *Petticoat Junction*?

C36 Who played Buffalo Bill Junior?

C37 The character Sir Willoughby Dodd appeared in which science fiction series?

C38 Which girl touched a wishing flower on her dress to make her dreams come true?

C39 Who was the hero of *Royal Canadian Mounted Police*?

C40 Who was the Stranger in the Australian sci-fi series of that name?

CAR 54, WHERE ARE YOU? OFFICERS

☞ Officer Gunther Toody
☞ Officer Francis Muldoon
☞ Captain Martin Block
☞ Officer Leo Schnauser
☞ Officer Steinmetz
☞ Officer Kissel
☞ Officer Ed Nicholson
☞ Desk Sgt Abrams

B1   Who created this rugged hero?

B2   John Noakes, seen here with his *Blue Peter* buddy Shep, found his way into the *Guinness Book of Records* for doing what?

B3   The Trumpton Fire Brigade leap into action. Who was their station officer?

B4 Which of Dr Who's enemies is pictured here?

B5 Which sci-fi family is shown here?

B6 Name the cool dude with the shooter.

B7 Who owned The Magic Roundabout?

47   Swashbucklers

A1 Who once broke his ankle as William Tell and had to play the part from a wheelchair?

A2 What was the Scarlet Pimpernel's real name?

A3 Which knight was played by William Russell?

A4 Who took the title role in *Arthur of the Britons*?

A5 Who was William Tell's fat foe?

B6 Which infamous highwayman was once played by Colin Edwin?

B7 Who played the Scarlet Pimpernel?

B8 Which series starred Edmund Purdom as Marco del Monte?

B9 What was the name of William Tell's burly accomplice, played by Nigel Greene?

B10 Who was Arthur of the Britons' principal rival?

C11 Which Dr Who starred in early BBC versions of *Robin Hood* and *Kidnapped*?

C12 Who was the Scarlet Pimpernel's arch enemy?

C13 What was the name of William Tell's wife?

C14 Who played Merlin in *The Adventures of Sir Lancelot*?

C15 What was Zorro's real name?

Pets Corner

*So many children's TV heroes have pets. They're always good
for a spot of pathos and can be relied upon to end up in life or
death situations which either necessitate them doing the
rescuing or being rescued. I suppose the strength of bond
between owner and pet depends on the amount of help the
animal is able to provide. It's all very well if you've got a
Lassie or a Fury, but I certainly wouldn't fancy being trapped
at the foot of a 300ft cliff with the tide rushing in fast,
knowing that my only means of salvation is Hammy
Hamster...*

*The owners below have lost their pets. Can you bring that ray
of sunshine back into their lives by matching them up?*

B1	Tintin	African Strangler, a man-eating plant
B2	Sebastian	Simba the lion
B3	Sexton Blake	Footso the cat
B4	Jimmy Wedgwood	Dusty the dog
B5	Gomez Addams	Packet the puppy
B6	Tex Tucker	Hamlet the hamster
B7	Twizzle	Belle the white dog
B8	The Jetsons	Snowy the dog
B9	Drooper	Judy the chimp
B10	The Brady Bunch	Aristotle the octopus
B11	Morticia Addams	Fletcher the flea
B12	Hank the cowboy	Tiger the shaggy dog
B13	Mrs Dingle	Silver King, a goofy horse
B14	Jungle Boy	Pedro the bloodhound
B15	Dr Marsh Tracy	Astro the dog.

49 Riding Through the Glen

*The Adventures of Robin Hood, which began in 1955, was one
of Lew Grade's first big successes, although the production itself
was anything but lavish. It was filmed on a studio set at
Walton-on-Thames, where the whole of Sherwood Forest was
played by a 20ft high hollow tree trunk on wheels which came
complete with its own fake mossy bank. For added authenticity,
the producers later built a second tree out of wood and plaster
which had a particularly fetching overhanging branch, just
right for Robin and co to launch themselves down on to the
unsuspecting Sheriff's men, who for some unaccountable reason
always chose that very spot to read* Ye Olde Sportinge Life.

A1 Who played Robin Hood?

A2 Who played the Sheriff of Nottingham?

A3 Who played Friar Tuck?

A4 Who was the principal actor to play Little John?

A5 Which two actresses played Maid Marian?

B6 Who graduated from Will Scarlett to Prime
Minister?

B7 Which actor was awarded the Queen's Medal for
Bravery after rescuing two children from a
bolting horse on the set?

B8 What was Robin's full name?

B9 Which sixties pop star was one of three actors to
play young Prince Arthur?

C10 Which popular children's presenter of the sixties
played Lady Coulchard?

C11 Which future *Steptoe and Son* star played
mathematics genius Nicodemus?

C12 What was Marian's surname?

C13 Which noted film director played Alan-a-Dale?

C14 Which game show host was cast as nobleman Sir
Walter?

50 Do Not Adjust Your Set

Comedy has always been an essential ingredient of British children's television, right back to the days of Mr Pastry *and* Billy Bunter *and carried on through the sixties by the likes of* Bonehead *and* Do Not Adjust Your Set. *But, of course, they were all upstaged by the* Blue Peter *elephant...*

A1 Who played Billy Bunter?

A2 What was *Mr Pastry*'s theme tune?

A3 Who played Captain Fantastic in *Do Not Adjust Your Set*?

A4 What did the Double Deckers use as their clubhouse?

A5 Who played Bonehead?

B6 Which buck-toothed Brummie became resident comic on *Crackerjack* in the sixties?

B7 Which comedy duo steered a Crazy Bus in the seventies?

B8 Who starred in *Just Jimmy*?

B9 Who was Bonehead's cheerless accomplice?

B10 Which well-known singer/impressionist began his career as a child performer on *Junior Showtime*?

C11 What was Mr Pastry's most celebrated routine?

C12 Which Australian comic joined *Crackerjack* in the late sixties?

C13 Which former *Coronation Street* actor starred with Hugh Paddick in *Pardon My Genie*?

C14 What was *Do Not Adjust Your Set*'s alternate title?

C15 Who compèred the variety show *Hopscotch*?

Family Ties

A1 In real life, what relation is *The Partridge Family*'s Shirley Jones to David Cassidy?

A2 In *Flipper*, what relation is Porter Ricks to Bud and Sandy?

A3 What relation was Marcia to Jan in *The Brady Bunch*?

A4 In *The Hillbilly Bears*, what relation was Flora to Paw Rugg?

A5 What relation was Virgil Tracy to Gordon in *Thunderbirds*?

B6 In *The Flintstones*, what relation is Bamm Bamm to the Rubbles?

B7 What relation was the first Dr Who to Susan Foreman?

B8 In *The Beverly Hillbillies*, what relation was Jethro to Jed Clampett?

B9 In *Bewitched*, what relation was Endora to Darrin?

B10 What relation is Elroy to George Jetson?

C11 What relation was Lucille Toody to Officer Gunther Toody in *Car 54, Where Are You*?

C12 In *Circus Boy*, what relation was Joey the clown to Corky?

C13 In *Kids from 47A*, what relation was Jess to Binny?

C14 What relation was Sandy to Ricky North in *Champion the Wonder Horse*?

C15 What relation is Noddy to Big Ears?

Bewitched

Particularly during the sixties, a number of American sitcoms cropped up on children's television in this country. This was mainly because what was considered mature, stylish comedy by the average sixties American was just about right for our twelve year-olds. I mean, Petticoat Junction *didn't exactly push back the barriers. It was no* Steptoe and Son. *Still, some were more than passable, and even watching* The Flying Nun *was better than doing maths homework.*

A1 Who was Darrin's boss in *Bewitched*?

A2 Who played the Flying Nun?

A3 Who starred in *Green Acres*?

A4 What was the name of the banker in *The Beverly Hillbillies*?

A5 Which future oil tycoon starred in *I Dream of Jeannie*?

B6 What number agent was played by Barbara Feldon in *Get Smart*?

B7 Who played Nanny in *Nanny and the Professor*?

B8 What was the name of the ghost played by Edward Mulhare in *The Ghost and Mrs Muir*?

B9 Airman Will Stockdale was the hero of which series?

B10 Who were the Stephens' next-door neighbours in *Bewitched*?

C11 Who starred as Julia in the American comedy series of that name?

C12 What was the name of the hotel run by Kate Bradley in *Petticoat Junction*?

C13 Who was the near-sighted lookout in *F Troop*?

C14 What was the Flying Nun's real name?

C15 Who played Granny Moses in *The Beverly Hillbillies*?

C16 What was the name of the family in *My Three Sons*?

C17 Who starred in *Father Knows Best*?

C18 Who was Lucy's best friend in *I Love Lucy*?

C19 What was the name of Toody and Muldoon's boss in *Car 54, Where Are You*?

C20 Who played My Favourite Martian?

MY FAVOURITE MARTIAN CHARACTERS

☞ Uncle Martin (the Martian)

☞ Tim O'Hara, reporter with the *Los Angeles Sun*

☞ Mrs Brown, O'Hara's landlady

☞ Angela Brown, her daughter

☞ Harry Burns, O'Hara's editor

53   Here's One I Made Earlier

When Blue Peter *began, on 16 October 1958, it was intended purely as a seven week experiment – a fifteen minute programme focussing on trains for boys and dolls for girls. The idea was that it would bridge the gap for five to eight year-olds who had grown out of* Watch With Mother *but were still too young to appreciate the BBC's major magazine programme,* Studio E. Blue Peter *creator John Hunter Blair gave the show a nautical title because he saw each programme as a voyage of adventure. How right he was!*

A1   Who became a *Blue Peter* presenter in 1962?

A2   What year was the Royal *Blue Peter* safari to Kenya?

A3   Which presenter was a dental nurse before joining *Blue Peter*?

A4   Who was *Blue Peter*'s animal expert from 1962 to 1988?

A5   What famous appendage was introduced in 1963?

B6   What is *Blue Peter*'s theme tune called?

B7   The adventures of which baby elephant were told and illustrated by Tony Hart in the early days of *Blue Peter*?

B8   In what year was the first *Blue Peter* appeal?

B9   Which puppy replaced Patch?

B10 Which presenter married singer Fred Mudd of The Muddlarks?

C11 In what year did Petra die?

C12 Which heavyweight political presenter once sabotaged the *Blue Peter* train set?

C13 Who designed the logo for the *Blue Peter* badge?

C14 Which young Royal prince came into the *Blue Peter* studio to fondle a lion cub?

C15 Which *Blue Peter* presenter had once been a chorus boy at the London Palladium?

BLUE PETER DISASTERS

☞ Lulu the baby elephant.

☞ Simon Groom eulogising over two door ornaments, "What a beautiful pair of knockers."

☞ John Noakes being knocked out by a 5lb imitation marrow.

☞ Christopher Trace splitting his trousers when bending down to feed England's largest pig.

☞ The girl guides' studio camp fire which suddenly produced 5ft flames and had to be hastily put out by the Fire Brigade.

☞ Mark Curry on his debut, treading on a 100 year-old tortoise that had 'fought' at Gallipoli.

That old showbusiness maxim about never appearing with children, animals or in an ITV sitcom certainly held true on Zoo Time, which was usually transmitted live from London Zoo. On one occasion, presenter Desmond Morris decided to take viewers on a tour of the big cat house, but to his acute embarrassment whichever lion the camera focused on immediately began to mate vigorously. His young audience was thus left in no doubt as to how the lion came to earn the title 'King of the Jungle'.

A1   Who presented *Animal Magic*?

A2   From which zoo was *Animal Magic* often broadcast?

A3   Which *Zoo Time* chimpanzee was such a talented artist that one of his paintings was bought by Picasso?

A4   Which husband and wife team used to take us *On Safari*?

A5   Which bird expert was a regular on *Animal Magic*?

B6   Who presented *Zoo Quest*?

B7   Which German husband and wife team went underwater in the 1956 series *Diving to Adventure*?

B8   Who introduced *Look*?

B9   Who succeeded Desmond Morris as presenter of *Zoo Time*?

B10 In what year did *Zoo Time* begin?
     a) 1956
     b) 1959
     c) 1964

C11 Who presented *Looking at Animals*?

C12 What nationality was the husband in number 4?

C13 Who used to explore the countryside on *Studio E*?

C14 Which animals does Johnny Morris say are the easiest to do voices for?
a) Gorillas
b) Camels
c) Centipedes

C15 Desmond Morris was once asked on *Zoo Time* that if all the animals in the zoo escaped, which one would the keepers be most frightened of? What was his answer?
a) Lion
b) Polar bear
c) Mossy sloth

WOMBLING SONGS

☞ The Wombling Song
☞ Remember You're a Womble
☞ Banana Rock
☞ Minuetto Allegretto
☞ Wombling Merry Christmas
☞ Wombling White Tie and Tails
☞ Super Womble
☞ Let's Womble to the Party Tonight

55   Wacky Racers

Pair up the Wacky Racers with their mixed-up machines.

B1 The Ant Hill Mob   The Bouldermobile

B2 Rufus Ruffcut and Sawtooth   The Army Surplus
                              Special

B3 Dick Dastardly and Muttley   The Creepy Coupe

B4 Peter Perfect   The Roaring Plenty

B5 Red Max   The Compact
                              Pussycat

B6 Sarge and Meekley   The Convert-A-Car

B7 The Slag Brothers   The Mean Machine

B8 Luke and Blubber   The Crimson
                              Haybailer

B9 Penelope Pitstop   The Buzz Wagon

B10 The Gruesome Twosome   The Varoom
                              Roadster

B11 Professor Pat Pending   The Arkansas
                              Chugga-Bug.

56 Bat Villain Wordsearch

Holy calamity! Some evil force has infiltrated eighteen Batvillains into this grid of Gotham City. And the fiendish mind that lies behind this dastardly deed has arranged the letters in such a way that they could be spelt out backwards or, and the word is almost too painful to speak, diagonally. Holy Concise Oxford Dictionary! Pray God that you find these villains before it is too late. To the Bat thesaurus!

```
T H E C U R E M A P A R K E R
H A F I S H F I N G E R S T A
E T T T O M R N A S T Y I H V
J S H H H D A E H G G E V E E
O I E E Z E E R F R M P T A N
K D N W S V M V O W A R H R A
E J R A G I T A P I R I E C M
R A Y S A L R E D S S N M H D
E M A H S H T E E H H C I E N
T E D M O U L T N Y A E N R A
S S C A T W O M A N S T S S S
K B O G G O F F D R O L T U G
U R N T H E F A R M L O R E N
N I T H E P E N G U I N E V R
K N I F E T H E R I D D L E R
```

57   Name the Personality

Identify the children's TV personalities from the clues given below.

B1   Involved in the early days of *Blue Peter*.
Introduced an award-winning programme for deaf children.
A talented artist.

B2   A great cartoon fan.
Had his own show featuring The Young Generation.
Renowned for his spontaneous paintings.

B3   Very tall and fairly Welsh.
Became Director of Television at the BBC.
Presented a popular 1950s series which encouraged children to parade their skills.

B4   First made his name with a Martian.
Puts words into other people's mouths.
His most famous creation is always the worse for wear.

B5   Used to front a skiffle group called The Vipers.
Was a regular on *Lift Off With Ayshea*.
Provided the voices of Ollie Beak, Joe Crow and Spike McPike.

B6   Born Cedric Lange.
Was once straight man to comedians such as Benny Hill, Arthur Askey and Norman Wisdom.
Hosted the popular noughts and crosses quiz on TV.

B7   Famed for playing a schoolboy.
Appropriately, he was called Fatty at school.
Now a successful restaurateur.

B8   Wrote the best-selling guitar manual *Play in a Day*.

Has backed such stars as Judy Garland, Frank Sinatra and Billy Fury.
A regular on *Tuesday Rendezvous* and *The Five O'Clock Club*.

B9 The BBC's most famous announcer.
An early host of *Come Dancing*.
Read the stories of Bengo.

B10 The only human face on *Watch With Mother*.
Was married to the late actor Duncan Lamont.
Put a smile on the faces of the Merrie Men .

B11 Played a TV announcer in the Peter Sellers film *I'm Alright Jack*.
Often seen with Pussy Cat Willum.
Went on to produce such shows as *Clapperboard*, *Lift Off With Ayshea* and *Get It Together*.

B12 Long-standing presenter of *Play School*.
Narrated *Trumpton* and *Camberwick Green*.
More recently presented *Bric-a-Brac*.

THE BANANA SPLITS

☞ Fleegle
☞ Bingo
☞ Drooper
☞ Snorky

B1 Who were described by a NASA scientist as "an attempt to bring a note of realism to the fantasy of the space race"?
a) *Thunderbirds*
b) *Pathfinders*
c) *Clangers*

B2 Who is being talked about here? "We stuck the drumsticks to his hands with jam. His natural reaction was to try and shake it off, so for a few seconds it looked as if he was really drumming."
a) Fred Barker
b) Dave Clark
c) Hammy Hamster

B3 Who is alleged to have once said: 'I just cannot believe how anybody can sell their soul and work with puppets"?
a) Rod Hull
b) Geoffrey Hayes
c) Jane Rossington

B4 Which children's favourite was once described by an irate director as "nothing but a bloody oven glove"?
a) Hartley Hare
b) Sooty
c) Roland Rat

B5 Who said about whom: "I often found myself wondering what he was thinking. Before every show, I washed his face and brushed his fur. If I accidentally dropped him, I immediately apologised"?
a) Marshall Thompson talking about Clarence the cross-eyed lion
b) Wally Whyton talking about Pussy Cat Willum
c) Harry Corbett talking about Sooty

B6 Who was being talked about here? "She would gum you to death if she got half a chance."
a) Petra
b) Skippy
c) Lassie

B7 Who confesses: "I was never given a *Crackerjack* pencil – but I still get asked for them today"?
a) Pip Hinton
b) Michael Aspel
c) Leslie Crowther

B8 Who described folk singer Jon Pertwee as an "old folker"?
a) Pete Murray
b) David Jacobs
c) Ollie Beak

B9 Who lamented: "I was totally identified with the part. Even when I travelled by air, customs officers used to look in my baggage and say, 'Any arrows to declare?'"?
a) Conrad Phillips
b) Alan Wheatley
c) David Nixon

B10 Which programme is being discussed here? "The board members of Associated-Rediffusion wouldn't dream of missing an episode. They used to interrupt their weekly meeting for a set to be wheeled in, just so that they could watch it."
a) *The Buccaneers*
b) *The Adventures of Sir Lancelot*
c) *Ivor the Engine*

59   Initial Problems

Can you solve the following clues with the help of the initials given?

A1   What B. is the bear in *Rainbow*?

A2   Which W.P. played Zoe in *Dr Who*?

A3   What F. was the womanising member of Boss Cat's gang?

A4   What W. was William Tell's son?

A5   Which D.D. played Elly May in *The Beverly Hillbillies*?

B6   What P.K. was a character in *Noggin the Nog*?

B7   What J.D. was an early sixties series about Dennis the Menace?

B8   What V. was a student pal of Scooby Doo?

B9   What P.B. was a character in *Captain Pugwash*?

B10   What S. was the identical cousin of Samantha in *Bewitched*?

C11   What H.H. was a series known in France as *La Maison de Tu Tu*?

C12   What G.T. was the street on which the Flintstones' home was situated?

C13   Which R.L. played Big Tim Champion in *Circus Boy*?

C14   What G.W. starred in *Inigo Pipkin*, forerunner to *Pipkins*?

C15   Which D.L. was played by Robert Adam in *Jungle Boy*?

C16   Which E.G. was a female compère of *Junior Criss Cross Quiz*?

C17   Which R.W. provided the music in the early days of *The Five O'Clock Club*?

C18 Which E.J. was a regular instructor on *Seeing Sport*?

C19 What J.H. was 'the surest and fastest shot in Africa'?

C20 Which A.H. was always so engrossed in his artistic work that a gong had to be sounded to tell him that the programme was about to end?

DEPUTY DAWG'S THREE FAVOURITE EXPLETIVES

☞ "Dagnamit!"
☞ "Just a cotton-pickin' minute."
☞ "Oooo, my toe-bone!"

Vince the gopher's catchphrase:
☞ "Can't see too well above ground."

---

60   Wombling Free

A1   Who narrates *The Wombles*?
a) Anthony Hopkins
b) Bernard Cribbins
c) Vincent Price

A2   Where do the Wombles live?
a) Wimbledon Common
b) Dartmoor
c) Wormwood Scrubs

A3   What do the Wombles insist on clearing from their grassy home?
a) Courting couples
b) Vehicles parked without displaying a current tax disc
c) Litter

A4   Which Womble is also the name of a city in New Zealand?
a) Auckland
b) Christchurch
c) Wellington

B5   Who created *The Wombles*?
a) Elisabeth Beresford
b) Oliver Postgate
c) Serge Danot

B6   In what year did The Wombles have their first hit?
a) 1972
b) 1974
c) 1977

B7 Which Womble is named after a South American river?
a) Plate
b) Orinoco
c) Amazon

B8 Which Womble wears a black bowler hat?
a) Bungo
b) Tobermory
c) Great Uncle Bulgaria

C9 Which Womble takes her name from an Australian city?
a) Miss Adelaide
b) Millie Melbourne
c) Alice Springs

C10 Who was the musical genius behind The Wombles' chart success?
a) Mike Batt
b) Mike Mansfield
c) Pete Townshend

C11 Which Womble is also the name of a Russian town?
a) Orsk
b) Omsk
c) Tomsk

C12 Which Womble takes her name from a town in western France?
a) Madame le Mans
b) Madame Cholet
c) Mademoiselle Rochefort-sur-Mer

61   The Oldest Swinger in Town

You can't beat a good imported adventure series. Clean cut heroes, plenty of dust and the odd moral thrown in, too. Nowadays, Tarzan would be lamenting the destruction of his rain forest and demanding to know how much was demolished to make Long John Silver's crutch. The tough truckers in Cannonball *would probably be eating muesli and if the Flashing Blade was still flashing, I expect he'd have a social worker on his case.*

A1 Who played Tarzan on TV?
A2 Who starred in *Sea Hunt*?
A3 In which country was *Whiplash* set?
A4 Which action packed series featured the exploits of helicopter pilots Chuck Martin and P.T. Moore?
A5 What daring pursuit was practised in *Ripcord*?

B6 Who starred in *Whiplash*?
B7 Which 1960 series was endorsed by the Mounties for its accurate portrayal of their work?
B8 Who played the marshal of Tombstone in *The Life and Legend of Wyatt Earp*?
B9 In which country was *The Forest Rangers* set?
B10 Who were the two central characters in *Ripcord*?

C11 Which two actors starred in *Cannonball*?
C12 During filming for which series was a complete village set washed away by torrential rain?
C13 What is the connection between the actor in number 6 and the star of *Gunsmoke*?
C14 Who was billed as 'the fastest girl gunslinger in the West'?
C15 Who succeeded Chuck Lambert as the pilot in *Ripcord*?

Time for Bed...

Of all the programmes shown in the 5.40 slot during the sixties, The Magic Roundabout *was the one which really acquired cult status. When it was taken off in 1968, an army camp bombarded the BBC with a petition for its return. Students lapped it up and there were even reports that a woman in Macclesfield had named her offspring Zebedee.*

A1 What was the name of *The Magic Roundabout*'s mighty mollusc?

A2 Who narrated the stories in the sixties?

A3 And who is his actress daughter?

A4 What kind of animal is Babar?

A5 What is Crystal Tipps' dog called?

B6 What is the name of the cow in *The Magic Roundabout*?

B7 How does Zebedee announce his entrance?

B8 Who narrated *Roobarb and Custard*?

B9 From which country did *Hector's House* originate?

B10 Who is *The Magic Roundabout*'s laid-back bunny?

C11 Besides Florence, who is the other girl in *The Magic Roundabout*?

C12 What was Nellie always doing in *Noah and Nellie*?

C13 Who was Noggin the Nog's Eskimo bride?

C14 Which *Magic Roundabout* character has a shaggy beard and wears a tall black hat?

C15 What was the name of the strange bird in Noggin the Nog?

63   Dr Who Crossword

Across

1 Surname of the first Doctor to encounter the Daleks. (8)

4 Snake-like creature from the planet Manussa. (4)

6 Female villain from the Colin Baker/Sylvester McCoy eras. (4)

8 Foe played by Philip Madoc in the 1968-69 story *The Krotons*. (4)

9 First name of the fourth Doctor. (3)

10 Did a car lead this enemy of the third Doctor? (6)

13 Played by Stephen Thorne, he caused havoc in *The Three Doctors*. (5)

14 Like Borusa, 13 across was a renegade Time ___. (4)

17 Played by Tom Watson and appeared in the 1967 story *The Underwater Menace*. (4)

19 Surname of actor who played the Master for many years. (7)

20 In a 1957 sitcom, 1 across used to be in this branch of the armed forces. (4)

21 See 15 down.

23 Doctor's female assistant who first appeared in *The Rescue* in 1965. (5)

24 It looked like a police box but... (6)

Down

1 Played 1 across in *The Five Doctors*. (8)

2 Warrior girl assistant of Tom Baker. (5)

3 ___ Manning played the leggy Ms Grant. (4)

5 Surname of actress who played Ace. (6)

7 See 11 down.

11 and 7 down Former gag writer for Tony Hancock and the man who created the Daleks. (5, 6)

12 Intelligent prehistoric race who battled with Jon Pertwee in 1970. (9)

15 and 21 across Actor who played the second Doctor. (7, 9)

16 First name of Jon Pertwee's second female assistant. (2)

18 Oedipus would have had a complex about these creatures. (7)

19 This female assistant was no ordinary bird – she was extinct. (4)

22 Before playing Mike Gambit, this actor was trapped on Metebelis 3 in *Planet of the Spiders* (surname). (4)

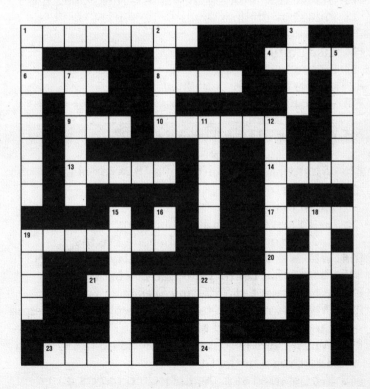

A1 Which former Radio 1 disc jockey presented *Multi-Coloured Swap Shop*?

A2 Which bear was a lousy comedian in *The Muppets*?

A3 Who played the Fonz in *Happy Days*?

A4 Which nineties movie star appeared in *Luna*?

A5 Which 1979 children's comedy centred around a robot?

A6 Who played Blake in *Blake's 7*?

A7 Complete the title: *Cloppa* ___.

A8 Which indefatigable young actress played Violet Elizabeth Bott in the 1976 production of *Just William*?

A9 In *The Muppet Show*, who was the manic drummer with the Electric Mayhem Band?

A10 And who fronted the band?

A11 In *H.R. Pufnstuf*, what was the name of Jimmy's talking flute?

A12 Who played Dick Turpin in 1979?

B13 What was the ambition of a 103 year-old man on *Jim'll Fix It*?
a) To make 104
b) To drive a Formula One racing car
c) To go on a date with Michelle Pfeiffer

B14 Who was the Brady Bunch's nutty housekeeper?

B15 From what century did Catweazle originate?

B16 Who presented *Saturday Scene*?

B17 Which two time detectives were played by Joanna Lumley and David McCallum?

B18 Which radio hero came to television in 1979 with Tony Vogel in the title role?

B19 Who starred as Luke Firbeck in *Luke's Kingdom*?

B20 Which Grange Hill pupil overcame heroin addiction?

B21 What was the name of the lazy cloth cat who lay on a cushion in a shop window?

B22 Who was the 'Matthew' in *Rainbow*'s early singing trio Rod, Jane and Matthew?

B23 Who was the evil witch in *H.R. Pufnstuf*?

B24 Which former screen sex goddess appeared in *Just William* in 1976?

C25 In Jamie, how did the young hero travel through time?

C26 Which of Worzel Gummidge's friends created him?

C27 In the 1979 series, who was Dick Turpin's young partner-in-crime?

C28 Which bouncy presenter asked us to *Think of a Number*?

C29 Who was Catweazle's companion Cedric the son of?

C30 Which Muppet character was said to be physically modelled on Lew Grade?

C31 Which Herbs character would have gone well with Larry the Lamb?

C32 In *Blake's 7*, which blonde gunslinger was played by Glynis Barber?

C33 With whom did Rudolf Nureyev dance *a pas de deux* on *The Muppets*?

C34 In *Happy Days*, what was Potsie's real name?

C35 What kind of animal was Mumfie?

C36 Who was transformed into ace detective Hong Kong Phooey?

C37 Who did Lorraine Chase play in *Worzel Gummidge*?

C38 Which sea-lion had its own series from 1974?

C39 What was the name of the village squire, played by Iain Cuthbertson, in *Children of the Stones*?

C40 Which mauve puppet was an early member of the *Rainbow* team?

THE MAGIC ROUNDABOUT CHARACTERS

☞ Florence
☞ Dougal
☞ Zebedee
☞ Mr Rusty
☞ Mr Machenry
☞ Brian
☞ Ermintrude
☞ Dylan
☞ Paul
☞ Basil
☞ Rosalie

---

65   Famous Sidekicks

Good things always come in pairs – like Laurel and Hardy, Abbott and Costello, gin and tonic. These questions refer to some of the finest double acts known to man.

A1 Who was Secret Squirrel's partner?

A2 What was the name of Jimmy Gibson's monkey in *Supercar*?

A3 What was the name of Quick Draw McGraw's trusty sidekick?

A4 Which of Deputy Dawg's assistants used to lament: "Can't see too well above ground"?

A5 Who was helped by Gurth?

B6 Tinker joined forces with which celebrated detective?

B7 What was the name of the white dolphin used as a means of transport by Marine Boy?

B8 Which animal was befriended by Sonny Hammond?

B9 Whose companions were Llud and Kai?

B10 Who was Astronut's Earth pal?

C11 Which little Indian boy accompanied Jonny Quest on his adventures?

C12 Which reporter toured the world with Hiram Holliday?

C13 What was the name of Hector Heathcote's faithful dog?

C14 Who was Bonehead's clumsy accomplice?

C15 In number 5, what was the name of Gurth's son?

66   The Doctor's Guests

All manner of people used to crop up in Dr Who. *Early sightings included* Crackerjack's *very own Peter Glaze as a Sensorite and, at the other end of the screen, lanky* Carry On *star Bernard Bresslaw as an Ice Warrior. More recently, Michael Melia, before going on to play hapless publican Eddie Royle in* EastEnders, *appeared as the leader of the Terileptils. Although the Terileptils were responsible for various atrocities, including the spread of the Great Plague, surely even they would have refused to drink with Pete Beale.*

How many of these Dr Who *guest stars do you remember?*

A1   Which newsreader, who went on to help Anneka Rice, played himself in the 1966 story *The War Machines*?

A2   Which avenging coffee-shaker played Arak in the 1974 adventure *Planet of the Spiders*?

A3   Which Monty Python star played an art critic in *City of Death* (1979)?

A4   Which latter-day Robin Hood was the rebellious Jondar in *Vengeance on Varos* (1985)?

A5   Which 'fat bastard' knew his stuff when playing a disc jockey in the 1985 story *Revelation of the Daleks*?

B6   Which actress, who later starred opposite Patrick Swayze, appeared as Samantha Briggs in *The Faceless Ones* (1971)?

B7   Which female impressionist was Flast, the Cryon leader, in *Attack of the Cybermen* (1985)?

B8   One of her followers, Varne, was played by a former *Blue Peter* presenter. Who was she?

B9 Which dirty-dealing *EastEnder* was seen as Kiston in the 1984 story *Resurrection of the Daleks*?

B10 Which upright *Porridge* custodian played Dr Quinn in *Dr Who and the Silurians* (1970)?

C11 Which comedy duo appeared as Harvey and Len in *Survival* (1989)?

C12 Which *Crossroads* stalwart played Elgin in the 1973 adventure *The Green Death*?

C13 Which long-suffering *EastEnder* was Eleanor in *The Time Warrior* (1973)?

C14 Which *Bread* star played Chela in the 1983 story *Snakedance*?

C15 Which *Coronation Street* regular was Jack Tyler in *Image of the Fendahl* (1977)?

NOGGIN THE NOG CHARACTERS

☞ Noggin the Nog
☞ Nogbad the Bad
☞ Nooka
☞ Thor Nogson
☞ Prince Knut
☞ Olaf the Lofty
☞ The Graculus

67 Train of Thought

The following questions are all based on trains.

A1 Who lived in Ivor the Engine's boiler?

A2 Who was Ivor's engine driver?

A3 What colour was the train in *The Magic Roundabout*?

A4 Who was the stationmaster in *Ivor the Engine*?

A5 In which country was *Ivor the Engine* set?

B6 Railroad supervisor Bart McClelland was the hero of which adventure series?

B7 What was Ivor the Engine's great ambition?

B8 Which *Blue Peter* presenter played with a model train set throughout his interview – and got the job?

B9 Which *Ivor the Engine* character was a mainstay of the local choir?

B10 The music to which fifties pop show began 'Over the points, over the points, over the points'?

C11 Which pair presented *Railway Roundabout*?

C12 Who played Bart McClelland in number 6?

C13 Who wrote *The Railway Children*?

C14 Which regular contributor to *Jackanory*, who had a sixties hit with 'Right Said Fred', starred in the 1970 film version of *The Railway Children*?

C15 For which railway company did Ivor the Engine work?

Time to Go Home

Yes, children, it's time to go home now. But first, here is one last quiz – about programming for the very young. We know a song about that, don't we children? And we'll probably sing it – in the street beneath the window of the neighbours we don't get on with.

A1 Whose footsteps did Bill and Ben dread hearing?

A2 What kind of animal was Mr Guinea Pig in *Tales of the Riverbank*? (Clue: This is not a trick question.)

A3 Which bowler-hatted character began each adventure in a costume shop?

A4 Who owned the magic shop in *Bagpuss*?

A5 Which lion was the star of *The Herbs*?

B6 What was the name of the doll in *Bagpuss*?

B7 In *Camberwick Green*, who ran Pippin Fort?

B8 Which boy's father ran a cafe near a lorry park?

B9 What kind of animal was Barnaby?

B10 Name the Trumpton firefighters (in order).

C11 What was the name of the tortoise in *The Flowerpot Men*?

C12 Who wrote the stories of *Rag, Tag and Bobtail*?

C13 Who was the bargee in *Chigley*?

C14 What was Mexican Pete's favourite dance on *Whirligig*?

C15 Which children's television announcer of the early fifties went on to become a film star in movies such as *The Beauty Jungle*?

Answers

1 LADY PENELOPE'S FAB 20

A1 A pink Rolls-Royce • **A2** FAB 1 • **A3** Five
A4 Tracy Island • **A5** Jeff Tracy • **A6** Brains
A7 The Hood • **B8** Scott • **B9** Virgil • **B10** Alan
B11 Gordon • **B12** John • **B13** The Mole • **C14** Kyrano
C15 Half-brother • **C16** Thunderizer • **C17** 2063
C18 David Graham • **C19** Creighton-Ward
C20 Bob Monkhouse

Final score ☐

2 THE GERRY ANDERSON TAPES

A1 *Captain Scarlet and the Mysterons*
A2 Stanley Unwin • **A3** Tex Tucker • **A4** On the front
of his hat • **A5** He could stretch his arms and legs
B6 Titan • **B7** Joe McClaine • **B8** Topsy Turvy Land
B9 Nicholas Parsons • **B10** Michael Holliday
B11 Rupert Davies • **C12** Rhapsody, Melody,
Symphony, Harmony, Destiny • **C13** World Aquanaut
Security Patrol • **C14** Slim Jim • **C15** The Orange Peel
Palace • **C16** Chawky • **C17** Mrs Appleby • **C18** Brain
Impulse Galvanascope Record and Transfer
C19 Dr Fawn • **C20** Sam Loover

Final score ☐

3 HAPPY FAMILIES
A1 Ben • **A2** Bobtail • **A3** Teddy • **A4** Jerry • **A5** Boo Boo
B6 Doggie Daddy • **B7** Quackers • **B8** Custard
B9 Tucker • **B10** Dixie • **C11** Midge • **C12** Nellie
C13 Mick • **C14** Booster • **C15** Alistair
Final score ☐

4 FROM BOOK TO SCREEN
A1 Peter Wyngarde • **A2** Dennis Waterman
A3 Jenny Agutter • **A4** Rupert • **A5** Parp parp
B6 Neville Whiting • **B7** Michael Bond
B8 Marmalade • **B9** Stacy Dorning
B10 Captain W.E. Johns • **C11** Fredric March
C12 Prunella Scales • **C13** Wemmick
C14 Arthur Lowe • **C15** John Leyton
Final score ☐

5 SPOT THE TUNE
A1 *The Adventures of Robin Hood*
A2 *The Beverly Hillbillies* • **A3** *The Banana Splits*
A4 *Boss Cat* • **A5** *Magpie* • **B6** *The Buccaneers*
B7 *Andy Pandy* • **B8** *The Monkees* • **B9** *The Wombles*
('Wombling Free') • **C10** *Pinky and Perky*
C11 *Flipper* • **C12** *Ivanhoe* • **C13** *The Addams Family*
Final score ☐

6 THE TRUMPTON JOB CENTRE
B1 Chippy Minton - carpenter • **B2** Nick Fisher -
bill poster • **B3** Mrs Dingle - postmistress
B4 Micky Murphy - baker • **B5** Thomas Tripp -
milkman • **B6** Mr Clamp - greengrocer

B7 Mrs Cobbit - flower seller • **B8** Mr Platt - clockmaker • **B9** Mr Craddock - park-keeper
B10 Mr Brackett - butler to Lord Belborough
B11 Mr Carraway - fishmonger • **B12** Roger Varley - chimney sweep • **B13** Raggy Dan - rag and bone man
B14 Mr Antonio - ice cream man • **B15** Mr Troop - town clerk
Final score ☐

7 TISWAS TEASERS

A1 Today is Saturday, Wear a Smile (I will also graciously accept Today is Saturday, Watch and Smile, which has been used on occasion) • **A2** Lenny Henry
A3 *OTT* • **A4** Over the top • **A5** The Phantom Flan Flinger • **B6** Sally James • **B7** John Gorman
B8 Cough the Cat • **B9** Sylvester McCoy
B10 Chris Tarrant • **C11** Chris Tarrant and John Asher • **C12** The *Tiswas* Twins
C13 Gordon Astley • **C14** c) 690 litres • **C15** b) 900
Final score ☐

8 PORK SCRATCHINGS

A1 Perky • **A2** The Beakles • **A3** Pinky (Perky wore blue) • **A4** 'We Belong Together' • **A5** Basil
B6 John Slater • **B7** Bertie Bonkers • **B8** Vera Vixen **B9** Conchita • **B10** Fred Emney • **C11** a) 1963
C12 *The Ed Sullivan Show* • **C13** Morton
C14 PPC TV • **C15** Ambrose
Final score ☐

9 BLUE PETER CROSSWORD

Across 1 Singleton • **5** PD (Peter Duncan) • **7** Lulu
8 Cat • **9** Backed • **11** Jason • **12** Shep • **15** Two
16 Patch • **19** Noakes • **20** Oct • **21** Alec • **23** Baxter
(Biddy) • **25** Rags • **26** Mark (Curry)
Down 1 Sticky • **2** No • **3** Trace • **4** Sundin • **5** Purves
6 Petra • **9** Barney • **10** Heston (Charlton) • **13** Heath
14 Freda • **15** Tina • **17** Anne • **18** Honey • **22** Car
24 Tim

10 LAND OF IRWIN ALLEN

A1 The Robinsons • **A2** Seaview • **A3** Spindrift
A4 The Bloop • **A5** Richard Basehart • **B6** Dr Zachary
Smith • **B7** a) The Titanic • **B8** c) Twelve times
B9 David Hedison • **B10** Doug Phillips and Tony
Newman • **C11** a) 1997 • **C12** Walter Pidgeon and
Robert Sterling • **C13** Inspector Kobick • **C14** Billy the
Kid • **C15** Jupiter 2
Final score ☐

11 SMARTER THAN THE AVERAGE BEAR

A1 Pebbles • **A2** Snickering • **A3** *Top Cat* • **A4** Spinach
A5 Jellystone • **B6** Great Dane • **B7** Hector Heathcote
B8 Granny Sweet • **B9** Officer Dibble • **B10** Duck
C11 George • **C12** Rugg • **C13** Squiddly Diddly
C14 Moose • **C15** Royal Order of Water Buffalos
Final score ☐

12 WHO'S ASSISTANTS

A1 Jamie • **A2** The sixth and seventh (Colin Baker and Sylvester McCoy) • **A3** Bonnie Langford • **A4** K9 **A5** Lethbridge-Stewart • **B6** Louise Jameson • **B7** Peter Purves • **B8** Herriot • **B9** Tegan • **B10** Peri **C11** Maureen O'Brien • **C12** Liz Shaw • **C13** Victoria Waterfield • **C14** Matthew Waterhouse • **C15** *The Ribos Operation*
Final score ☐

13 CONNECTIONS

A1 Muffin appeared with Annette Mills, whose actor brother John starred in the film *Ryan's Daughter*.
A2 Peter Hawkins provided voices for both.
A3 The gardener in *The Herbs* is Mr Bayleaf and Bayleaf is a character in *London's Burning*.
A4 Rodney Bewes, star of *The Likely Lads*, was one of Basil Brush's straight men. • **A5** William Russell, who played Sir Lancelot, was schoolteacher Ian Chesterton in the opening episode of *Dr Who*. • **B6** Michael Crawford, who played Frank, was one of the boys in *Billy Bunter*. • **B7** Susan Dey, alias Laurie Partridge, is Grace Van Owen in *LA Law*. • **B8** Both are the voice of Daws Butler. • **B9** *Rainbow*'s Geoffrey Hayes played DC Scatliff in *Z Cars*. • **B10** The voice of Captain Scarlet was Francis Matthews, who went on to play TV detective Paul Temple. • **C11** One of the hosts of *Junior Criss Cross Quiz* was Bill Grundy, who later conducted the infamous four-letter interview with The Sex Pistols. • **C12** Susan Stranks was on the first panel of *Juke Box Jury* as 'a typical teenager' before

going on to present *Magpie*. • **C13** Davy Jones of The Monkees once played Ena Sharples' grandson in *Coronation Street*. • **C14** Bowie's father ran the Lenny the Lion fan club and young David was a big fan too. **C15** Wally Whyton, who did the voice of Ollie Beak, had once busked in the south of France where his 'bottler' (the person who collects the money) was Jacques Tati.

Final score ☐

14 HI-YO SILVER!

A1 Clayton Moore • **A2** Pancho • **A3** Chingachgook **A4** Davy Crockett • **A5** Kemo sabe • **B6** William Boyd **B7** Zorro • **B8** 'Home on the Range' • **B9** Fess Parker **B10** Black • **C11** Lacrosse • **C12** Guy Madison **C13** John Reid • **C14** The Melody Ranch • **C15** Gail Davis

Final score ☐

15 HUMAN PARTNERS

A1 Derek Fowlds • **A2** Jean Morton • **A3** Ken Dodd **A4** Michael Bentine • **A5** Muriel Young • **B6** Ray Alan **B7** Larry Parker • **B8** Peter Brough • **B9** Wilbur Post **B10** Ricky North • **C11** Dorothy Smith • **C12** Saveen **C13** Molly Blake • **C14** Ken McLaughlin **C15** Humphrey Lestocq

Final score ☐

16 SUPERHEROES

A1 Clark Kent • **A2** Adam West • **A3** Spiderman
A4 Bruce Wayne • **A5** Alfred • **B6** Professor Mariner
B7 Krypton • **B8** Commissioner Gordon
B9 Peter Parker • **B10** Crabbe • **C11** Neptina
C12 Jack Larson • **C13** Executive producer William
Dozier • **C14** Smallville • **C15** Ocean Patrol
Final score ☐

17 IZZY WHIZZY, LET'S GET BUSY!

A1 Xylophone • **A2** Sweep • **A3** Oofle Dust • **A4** Soo
A5 The Sooteries • **B6** Ramsbottom • **B7** Gerry Marsden
of Gerry and the Pacemakers • **B8** Oxo • **B9** Kipper
B10 c) £20,000 • **C11** *Saturday Special*
C12 Peter Butterworth • **C13** Gilbert Harding
C14 The newspapers carried a story about a boy who
imitated Sooty and whacked his dad over the head with
a real hammer. Dad was carted off to hospital.
C15 c) Iron Maiden
Final score ☐

18 HOSTS WITH THE MOST

A1 Leila Williams • **A2** Chris Kelly
A3 Desmond Morris • **A4** Stubby Kaye
A5 Fred Dinenage • **B6** Freddie Garrity
B7 Peter Lloyd • **B8** Adrian Hill • **B9** Bobby Bennett
B10 Billy Wright • **C11** Neville Whiting
C12 Roger Whittaker • **C13** Eamonn Andrews
C14 Alex Macintosh • **C15** James Fisher
Final score ☐

19 PIECES OF EIGHT
A1 The Black Pig • **A2** Robert Shaw • **A3** Dan Tempest
A4 Long John Silver • **A5** Tom • **B6** Terence Morgan
B7 Lieutenant Beamish • **B8** Captain Haddock
B9 Cut Throat Jake • **B10** The Sultana
C11 Kit Taylor • **C12** *Sailor of Fortune* • **C13** Jean Kent
C14 Dickon • **C15** The Spaniards
Final score ☐

20 NAME THE YEAR
C1 1960 • **C2** 1955 • **C3** 1969 • **C4** 1962 • **C5** 1974
C6 1958 • **C7** 1967 • **C8** 1952 • **C9** 1972 • **C10** 1964
Final score ☐

21 EDUCATIONALLY SPEAKING
A1 John Craven • **A2** *Vision On* • **A3** Tony Hart
A4 Jack Hargreaves • **A5** Geoffrey Wheeler
B6 Danny Blanchflower • **B7** Barry Bucknell
B8 *Railway Roundabout* • **B9** Graham Dangerfield
B10 Jimmy Hanley • **C11** Wendy Dickeson
C12 Bill Salmon • **C13** Huw Thomas
C14 Serendipity Dog • **C15** Cliff Morgan
Final score ☐

22 MONSTER MASH
A1 Lurch • **A2** Herman • **A3** Marilyn • **A4** Al Lewis
A5 Morticia • **B6** 1313 Mockingbird Lane
B7 Jackie Coogan • **B8** Lawyer • **B9** A bat
B10 *Car 54, Where Are You?* • **C11** Homer
C12 Gateman, Goodbury and Graves Funeral Directors
C13 Harpsichord • **C14** Butch Patrick • **C15** b) 378
Final score ☐

23 WATCH WITH MOTHER CROSSWORD

Across 1 Buttercup • **5** Clay • **7** Peter • **9** Slow
11 Driscoll • **12** Little • **15** Looby • **16** Bird
17 Hawkins • **21** Andy • **24** Loo • **25** Jenny • **26** Wed
Down 1 Bobtail • **2** Tag • **3** Rag • **4** *Picture Book*
5 Curbs • **6** Bill • **8** Spotty • **10** Weed • **13** Teddy
14 Pandy • **16** Basket • **18** Willy • **19** Sam • **20** Time
22 Dog • **23** Cow

24 PICTURE QUIZ NUMBER ONE

B1 Tin-Tin • **B2** Seeing the Queen's smart velvet
outfit, Harry Corbett decided that Sooty should squirt
Prince Philip instead. • **B3** Their long hair
B4 Double or Drop on *Crackerjack* • **B5** John Slater
B6 *Voyage to the Bottom of the Sea* • **B7** Clangers
B8 *Captain Scarlet and the Mysterons*
Final score ☐

25 THE FIFTIES

A1 The Bumblies • **A2** Michael Bentine
A3 The Fat Owl • **A4** Richard Hearne • **A5** *Mick and
Montmorency* • **A6** Knitting patterns • **A7** Yoo-hoo
A8 *Toytown* • **A9** John Hart • **A10** Dale Evans
A11 Mickey Braddock • **A12** Rocky
B13 Dale Robertson • **B14** Carroll Levis
B15 Fanny and Johnnie Cradock • **B16** Noddy
B17 Africa • **B18** Francis Coudrill • **B19** Mr Quelch
B20 b) Mischief • **B21** *The Appleyards*
B22 Big Tim Champion • **B23** Bullet • **B24** Jim Newton
B25 Steve Race • **C26** Alexander Gauge (who played
Friar Tuck) • **C27** *Young Hercules* • **C28** Harry Watt

C29 Rolf Harris • **C30** Jimmy Hanley • **C31** Frontier Doctor • **C32** Rex Allen • **C33** Richard O'Sullivan **C34** Minerva Urecal • **C35** Captain Horatio Bullwinkle **C36** Eamonn Andrews • **C37** Geoffrey Robinson **C38** Horace • **C39** Timothy • **C40** Vintage cars

Final score ☐

26 BATBUSTERS
A1 Harriet • **A2** (Cesar) Romero • **A3** (Alan) Napier **A4** Gotham • **A5** Dick (Grayson) • **B6** The Siren **B7** (Stafford) Repp • **B8** (Frank) Gorshin **B9** Barbara (Gordon) • **B10** The Penguin **C11** (Ty) Hardin • **C12** (Ida) Lupino • **C13** The Minstrel **C14** The Puzzler • **C15** Chandell

Final score ☐

27 FIRST NAMES
B1 Willy • **B2** Penelope • **B3** Alexander • **B4** Maisie **B5** Dill • **B6** Gabriel • **B7** Barney • **B8** George **B9** Jimmy • **B10** Slim • **B11** Cactus • **B12** Major Dennis **B13** Pat • **B14** Mike • **B15** Ted • **B16** Simon **B17** Janice • **B18** Frank • **B19** Kiki • **B20** Nogbad

Final score ☐

28 WHO'S WHO
A1 Shaw Taylor • **A2** Roy Castle • **A3** Jimmy Savile **A4** Mike Sarne • **A5** Johnny Morris • **B6** Sylvia Peters **B7** Percy Thrower • **B8** Pat Keysell • **B9** Jack Wild **B10** Robert Harbin • **C11** Lee Montague **C12** Gary Miller • **C13** Peter Butterworth **C14** Edward Andrews • **C15** Anita (Harris)

Final score ☐

29 FAMOUS SETTINGS

B1 *Hopalong Cassidy* - The Bar 20 • **B2** *Noddy* -
Toyland • **B3** *Pingwings* - Berrydown Farm
B4 *F Troop* - Fort Courage • **B5** *Rupert* - Nut Wood
B6 *Petticoat Junction* - Hooterville • **B7** *Superman* -
Metropolis • **B8** *The Tomorrow People* - The Lab
B9 *Twizzle* - Stray Town • **B10** *Stingray* - Marineville
B11 *The Buccaneers* - New Providence • **B12** *The
Adventures of William Tell* - Altdorf • **B13** *Daktari* -
Wameru Study Centre • **B14** *Fireball XL5* - Space City
B15 *Rin Tin Tin* - Fort Apache
Final score ☐

30 ODD ONE OUT

A1 c) Gerald the giraffe • **A2** b) John Cleese
A3 a) Dick Van Dyke • **A4** c) Thrednog the Thin
A5 c) Reg Varney • **B6** c) Sally James
B7 b) Thyme the clockmender • **B8** a) Mr Sheen
B9 b) Harry the horse • **B10** a) Captain Cerise
C11 b) Claire Rayner • **C12** b) Floppy • **C13** a) Steve
C14 b) Jeremy Paxman
Final score ☐

31 BOOM! BOOM!

A1 Ivan Owen • **A2** Terry-Thomas • **A3** Roy North
A4 Blast • **A5** Derek Fowlds • **B6** Peter Firmin
B7 *The Three Scampies* • **B8** McPike
B9 A Scottish hedgehog • **B10** Rodney Bewes
C11 David Nixon • **C12** a) 1968 • **C13** Inspector Bruce
C14 Billy Boyle • **C15** Howard Williams
Final score ☐

32 EARLY BREAKS
A1 David Jason • **A2** Liza Goddard • **A3** Anita Dobson
A4 David Cassidy • **A5** Roger Moore in *Ivanhoe*
B6 Mick Jagger • **B7** Michael Caine
B8 Stephanie Beacham • **B9** David Hemmings
B10 Jeremy Irons • **C11** Judi Dench
C12 Patrick McGoohan • **C13** Leslie Phillips
C14 Tim Curry
Final score ☐

33 MOVIE CLIPS
A1 Christopher Reeve • **A2** Jack Nicholson
A3 Robin Hood • **A4** *Thunderbirds Are Go*
A5 *The Magic Roundabout* • **B6** *Clarence the Cross-Eyed Lion* • **B7** Frances de la Tour • **B8** Manhattan
B9 *City of Gold* • **B10** c) 1979 • **C11** *Head* • **C12** Peter
Cushing • **C13** Elizabeth Taylor • **C14** b) 1938
C15 Kirk Alyn
Final score ☐

34 CATCHPHRASES
A1 Parker in *Thunderbirds* • **A2** Lurch in *The Addams
Family* • **A3** Fred Flintstone • **A4** *Batman*
A5 *The Adventures of Superman* • **B6** Tingha and
Tucker • **B7** *The Banana Splits*
B8 Humphrey Lestocq • **B9** Snagglepuss
B10 Billy Bunter • **C11** Boss in *Bonehead*
C12 Huw Wheldon • **C13** Peter Lloyd on *Seeing Sport*
C14 Lenny the Lion • **C15** The Cisco Kid
Final score ☐

35 PLAY SCHOOL PRESENTERS WORDSEARCH

```
A D I E M G R I F F I T H S W
I I D W U O E I N S T E I N L
R O A D N W B O V L I S F M N
C R O P R E J E M I M A G A O
D O G M O R T O N V T T H Y R
B I G T E D I M J J N R A A E
S T O A T U N A U C A U R L D
T M H T H C C J D H C M R L A
E I S O O K J O G E E P I T E
V N T G M O O S E L E N S N L
E O I A J P U L L L L A B O P
N G N Z O A S H C R O F T O Z
S U G Z N T T O S B O U R N E
V E G A E H L I N E K E R E B
Y A T E S L I T T L E T E D U
```

36 CREATIVE TALENTS

A1 Roberta Leigh • **A2** John Ryan • **A3** Bill Hanna and Joe Barbera • **A4** Gene Roddenberry • **A5** Bob Kane
B6 Frank Richards • **B7** John Ryan • **B8** Charles Addams • **B9** Michael Bond • **B10** Oliver Postgate and Peter Firmin • **C11** George Trendle • **C12** Jerome Siegel and Joe Shuster • **C13** Richard Carpenter
C14 Alison Uttley • **C15** John Hunter Blair
C16 David Ellison • **C17** Roberta Leigh • **C18** Hilary Hayton • **C19** King Rollo • **C20** Roger Price
Final score ☐

37 CHILDREN'S DRAMA

A1 Sam Kydd • **A2** *Crane* • **A3** Terence Alexander
(Charlie Hungerford in *Bergerac*) • **A4** Rhodes Reason
A5 The Voice • **B6** Laurence Payne • **B7** *Freewheelers*
B8 Brian Worth • **B9** *Adventure Weekly* • **C10** a) Boys
b) War • c) Spur • **C11** *The Forest Rangers*
C12 Hiram Holliday • **C13** The Gizzmo
C14 The Grey Panther • **C15** Four

Final score ☐

38 NAME THE SHOW

A1 *The Telegoons* • **A2** *Tich and Quackers*
A3 *Record Breakers* • **B4** *Top of the Form*
B5 *The Five O'Clock Club* • **B6** *Play School*
B7 *Clangers* • **C8** *Kids from 47A* • **C9** *Chigley*
C10 *Richard the Lionheart* • **C11** *Follyfoot*
C12 *The Singing Ringing Tree*

Final score ☐

39 IT'S FRIDAY, IT'S FIVE TO FIVE...

A1 Eamonn Andrews • **A2** *Crackerjack* pencils
A3 Double or Drop • **A4** A cabbage • **A5** Michael Aspel
B6 Peter Glaze • **B7** Ronnie Corbett
B8 Leslie Crowther • **B9** Ed Stewart • **B10** Stewpot
C11 Christine Holmes • **C12** Joe Baker and Jack
Douglas • **C13** Bert Hayes • **C14** Christine Holmes
C15 Eamonn Andrews

Final score ☐

40 SCI-FI

A1 Geoffrey Bayldon • **A2** The Wedgwood family
A3 John • **A4** Roddy McDowall • **A5** Tarot • **B6** Carrot
B7 Aegira • **B8** Galen • **B9** Ozymandias • **B10** Flintlock
C11 St Oswald • **C12** Platonus • **C13** *Stranger from
Space* • **C14** Mark Bannerman • **C15** The Winter family
Final score ☐

41 POP POSERS

A1 b) The Bay City Rollers • **A2** b) 'I'm a Believer'
A3 b) Brough • **A4** c) Elvis Presley • **B5** b) Megg Nicoll
B6 b) Mike Nesmith • **B7** a) Arrows • **B8** b) The Turtles
C9 c) Alan Price • **C10** b) Billy J. Kramer • **C11** a) *The
Count of Monte Cristo* • **C12** b) Danny Bonaduce
Final score ☐

42 TO BOLDLY GO

A1 Vulcan • **A2** Bones • **A3** Montgomery • **A4** Japanese
A5 Lt Uhura • **B6** Tiberius • **B7** Gerald Ford
B8 Walter Koenig • **B9** The Romulans • **B10** The
Yorktown • **C11** The Medusans • **C12** 512 • **C13** Majel
Barrett • **C14** Robert T. April • **C15** Captain Pike
Final score ☐

43 CARTOON CROSSWORD

Across 1 Clementine • **3** Shag • **5** Bedrock • **8** Blanc
10 Lion • **11** Horse • **14** Slate • **15** Jetsons • **18** Wolf
19 Pink • **21** Horn • **24** Atom Ant • **25** Musky
Down 1 Choo-Choo • **2** Meeces • **4** Hill • **6** Oyl
7 Vince • **9** Augie • **12** Rubble • **14** Spook • **16** Scooby
17 Benny • **18** Wilma • **20** Dino • **22** Tom • **23** Pup

44 WHICH DOCTORS

A1 The third (Jon Pertwee) • **A2** The second
(Patrick Troughton) • **A3** The first (William Hartnell)
A4 The third (Jon Pertwee) • **A5** The fourth
(Tom Baker) • **B6** The fourth (Tom Baker)
B7 The fifth (Peter Davison) • **B8** The first
(William Hartnell) • **B9** The first (William Hartnell)
B10 The second (Patrick Troughton) • **C11** The fourth
(Tom Baker) • **C12** The sixth (Colin Baker)
C13 The fourth (Tom Baker) • **C14** The first (William
Hartnell) • **C15** The second (Patrick Troughton)
Final score ☐

45 THE SIXTIES

A1 *Danger Island* • **A2** Butch • **A3** *Magpie*
A4 Penguins • **A5** Patrick Moore • **A6** Za Za
A7 Topo Gigio • **A8** Shirley Abicair • **A9** Don Adams
A10 Husky • **A11** Davros • **A12** Hammy Hamster
B13 O'Connor • **B14** Joan Clarke • **B15** Leslie Crowther
B16 Oxy-gum • **B17** Roderick • **B18** Peter Hawkins
B19 McCrimmon • **B20** Stanley Dangerfield • **B21** Paula
B22 Wrangler Jane • **B23** France • **B24** Hope Lange
C25 World Intelligence Network • **C26** Katie Kookaburra
C27 Derek Nimmo • **C28** Robin Adler • **C29** Elwyn
Brook-Jones • **C30** A cartoon pop group who fought
crime • **C31** Alexis Korner • **C32** Lady Romanadvor-
atrelundar • **C33** Pierre Radisson • **C34** Oliver Air
Force Base • **C35** Billie Jo, Bobbie Jo, Betty Jo
C36 Dick West • **C37** *Sierra Nine* • **C38** Bizzy Lizzy
C39 Corporal Jacques Gagnier • **C40** Adam Suisse
(played by Ron Haddrich)
Final score ☐

46 PICTURE QUIZ NUMBER TWO

B1 Freda Lingstrom • **B2** Being the first British
civilian to make a 25,000ft free-fall parachute descent.
B3 Captain Flack • **B4** The Cybermen
B5 The Robinsons from *Lost in Space* • **B6** Tintin
B7 Mr Rusty

Final score ☐

47 SWASHBUCKLERS

A1 Conrad Phillips • **A2** Sir Percy Blakeney
A3 Sir Lancelot • **A4** Oliver Tobias • **A5** Landburgher
Gessler • **B6** Dick Turpin • **B7** Marius Goring
B8 *Sword of Freedom* • **B9** The Bear • **B10** Mark of
Cornwall • **C11** Patrick Troughton • **C12** Chauvelin
C13 Hedda • **C14** Cyril Smith • **C15** Don Diego de la Vega

Final score ☐

48 PETS CORNER

B1 Tintin – Snowy the dog • **B2** Sebastian – Belle the
white dog • **B3** Sexton Blake – Pedro the bloodhound
B4 Jimmy Wedgwood – Hamlet the hamster
B5 Gomez Addams – Aristotle the octopus
B6 Tex Tucker – Dusty the dog • **B7** Twizzle – Footso
the cat • **B8** The Jetsons – Astro the dog
B9 Drooper – Fletcher the flea • **B10** The Brady Bunch
– Tiger the shaggy dog • **B11** Morticia Addams –
African Strangler, a man-eating plant
B12 Hank the cowboy – Silver King, a goofy horse
B13 Mrs Dingle – Packet the puppy • **B14** Jungle Boy –
Simba the lion • **B15** Dr Marsh Tracy – Judy the chimp

Final score ☐

49 RIDING THROUGH THE GLEN

A1 Richard Greene • **A2** Alan Wheatley
A3 Alexander Gauge • **A4** Archie Duncan (Rufus
Cruikshank appeared in ten episodes) • **A5** Bernadette
O'Farrell and Patricia Driscoll • **B6** Paul Eddington –
he played Will Scarlett and, more recently, Jim
Hacker in *Yes, Prime Minister* • **B7** Archie Duncan
B8 Robin of Locksley • **B9** Peter Asher, half of pop duo
Peter and Gordon • **C10** Muriel Young • **C11** Harry H.
Corbett • **C12** Fitzwalter • **C13** John Schlesinger
C14 Nicholas Parsons
Final score ☐

50 DO NOT ADJUST YOUR SET

A1 Gerald Campion • **A2** 'Pop Goes the Weasel'
A3 David Jason • **A4** A bus • **A5** Colin Douglas
B6 Don MacLean • **B7** Hope and Keen
B8 Jimmy Clitheroe • **B9** Happy • **B10** Joe Longthorne
C11 The Lancers • **C12** Rod McLennan
C13 Roy Barraclough • **C14** *The Fairly Pointless Show*
C15 Jeremy Hawk
Final score ☐

51 FAMILY TIES

A1 Stepmother • **A2** Father • **A3** Sister • **A4** Daughter
A5 Brother • **B6** Adopted son • **B7** Grandfather
B8 Nephew • **B9** Mother-in-law • **B10** Son • **C11** Wife
C12 No relation – he was his guardian
C13 Elder sister • **C14** Uncle
C15 They don't have relations – they're just good friends
Final score ☐

52 BEWITCHED

A1 Larry Tate • **A2** Sally Field • **A3** Eddie Albert
A4 Milburn Drysdale • **A5** Larry Hagman
B6 Ninety-nine • **B7** Juliet Mills • **B8** Captain Gregg
B9 *No Time for Sergeants* • **B10** The Kravitzes
C11 Diahann Carroll • **C12** The Shady Rest Hotel
C13 Private Vanderbilt • **C14** Sister Bertrille
C15 Irene Ryan • **C16** Douglas • **C17** Robert Young
C18 Ethel Mertz • **C19** Captain Martin Block
C20 Ray Walston
Final score ☐

53 HERE'S ONE I MADE EARLIER

A1 Valerie Singleton • **A2** 1971 • **A3** Yvette Fielding
A4 George Cansdale • **A5** The *Blue Peter* badge
B6 'Barnacle Bill' • **B7** Packie • **B8** 1962 • **B9** Shep
B10 Leila Williams • **C11** 1977 • **C12** Richard Dimbleby
C13 Tony Hart • **C14** Prince Edward
C15 Peter Purves
Final score ☐

54 NATURAL HISTORY

A1 Johnny Morris • **A2** Bristol • **A3** Congo
A4 Armand and Michaela Denis • **A5** Tony Soper
B6 David Attenborough • **B7** Hans and Lotte Hass
B8 Peter Scott • **B9** Chris Kelly • **B10** a) 1956
C11 George Cansdale • **C12** Belgian • **C13** Ion Trant
C14 b) Camels • **C15** b) Polar bear
Final score ☐

55 WACKY RACERS

B1 The Ant Hill Mob – The Roaring Plenty

B2 Rufus Ruffcut and Sawtooth – The Buzz Wagon

B3 Dick Dastardly and Muttley – The Mean Machine

B4 Peter Perfect – The Varoom Roadster

B5 Red Max – The Crimson Haybailer

B6 Sarge and Meekley – The Army Surplus Special

B7 The Slag Brothers – The Bouldermobile

B8 Luke and Blubber – The Arkansas Chugga-Bug

B9 Penelope Pitstop – The Compact Pussycat

B10 The Gruesome Twosome – The Creepy Coupe

B11 Professor Pat Pending – The Convert-A-Car

Final score ☐

56 BAT VILLAIN WORDSEARCH

57 NAME THE PERSONALITY

B1 Tony Hart • **B2** Rolf Harris • **B3** Huw Wheldon
B4 Ray Alan • **B5** Wally Whyton • **B6** Jeremy Hawk
B7 Gerald Campion • **B8** Bert Weedon
B9 Sylvia Peters • **B10** Patricia Driscoll
B11 Muriel Young • **B12** Brian Cant
Final score ☐

58 QUICK QUOTES

B1 c) *Clangers* • **B2** c) Hammy Hamster
B3 b) Geoffrey Hayes • **B4** a) Hartley Hare
B5 c) Harry Corbett talking about Sooty • **B6** a) Petra
B7 c) Leslie Crowther • **B8** c) Ollie Beak
B9 b) Alan Wheatley – the Sheriff of Nottingham in
The Adventures of Robin Hood
B10 c) *Ivor the Engine*
Final score ☐

59 INITIAL PROBLEMS

A1 Bungle • **A2** Wendy Padbury • **A3** Fancy • **A4** Walter
A5 Donna Douglas • **B6** Prince Knut • **B7** Just Dennis
B8 Velma • **B9** Pirate Barnabus • **B10** Serena
C11 *Hector's House* • **C12** Greasepit Terrace
C13 Robert Lowery • **C14** George Woodbridge
C15 Doc Lawrence • **C16** Elaine Grand
C17 Roger Webb • **C18** Emlyn Jones • **C19** John Hunter,
hero of *White Hunter* • **C20** Adrian Hill, presenter of
Sketch Club
Final score ☐

60 WOMBLING FREE

A1 b) Bernard Cribbins • **A2** a) Wimbledon Common
A3 c) Litter • **A4** c) Wellington • **B5** a) Elisabeth
Beresford • **B6** b) 1974 • **B7** b) Orinoco
B8 b) Tobermory • **C9** a) Miss Adelaide • **C10** a) Mike
Batt • **C11** c) Tomsk • **C12** b) Madame Cholet
Final score ☐

61 THE OLDEST SWINGER IN TOWN

A1 Ron Ely • **A2** Lloyd Bridges • **A3** Australia
A4 *Whirlybirds* • **A5** Parachuting • **B6** Peter Graves
B7 *Royal Canadian Mounted Police* • **B8** Hugh O'Brian
B9 Canada • **B10** Ted McKeever and Jim Buckley
C11 Paul Birch and William Campbell • **C12** *Tarzan*
C13 Peter Graves is the brother of *Gunsmoke*'s James
Arness • **C14** Annie Oakley • **C15** Charlie Kern
Final score ☐

62 TIME FOR BED...

A1 Brian • **A2** Eric Thompson • **A3** Emma Thompson
A4 Elephant • **A5** Alistair • **B6** Ermintrude • **B7** Boing!
B8 Richard Briers • **B9** France • **B10** Dylan
C11 Rosalie • **C12** Niggling • **C13** Nooka
C14 Mr Rusty • **C15** The Graculus
Final score ☐

63 DR WHO CROSSWORD

Across **1** Hartnell • **4** Mara • **6** Rani • **8** Elek
9 Tom • **10** Autons • **13** Omega • **14** Lord • **17** Ramo
19 Delgado • **20** Army • **21** Troughton • **23** Vicki
24 TARDIS
Down **1** Hurndall • **2** Leela • **3** Katy • **5** Aldred
7 Nation • **11** Terry • **12** Silurians • **15** Patrick
16 Jo • **18** Mummies • **19** Dodo • **22** Hunt

64 THE SEVENTIES

A1 Noel Edmonds • **A2** Fozzie • **A3** Henry Winkler
A4 Patsy Kensit • **A5** *Metal Mickey* • **A6** Gareth Thomas
A7 *Castle* • **A8** Bonnie Langford • **A9** Animal
A10 Dr Teeth • **A11** Freddie • **A12** Richard O'Sullivan
B13 b) To drive a Formula One racing car
B14 Alice Nelson • **B15** The eleventh • **B16** Sally James
B17 Sapphire and Steel • **B18** Dick Barton
B19 Oliver Tobias • **B20** Zammo • **B21** Bagpuss
B22 Matthew Corbett • **B23** Miss Witchiepoo
B24 Diana Dors • **C25** On a magic carpet
C26 The Crowman • **C27** Swiftnick • **C28** Johnny Ball
C29 Lord and Lady Collingford
C30 Dr Bunsen Honeydew • **C31** Aunt Mint
C32 Soolin • **C33** Miss Piggy • **C34** Warren Weber
C35 Baby elephant • **C36** Henry the janitor
C37 Dolly Clothes-Peg • **C38** Salty • **C39** Hendrick
C40 Moony
Final score ☐

65 FAMOUS SIDEKICKS

A1 Morocco Mole • **A2** Mitch • **A3** Baba Looey
A4 Vince • **A5** Ivanhoe • **B6** Sexton Blake
B7 Splasher • **B8** Skippy • **B9** Arthur of the Britons
B10 Oscar • **C11** Hadji • **C12** Joel Smith • **C13** Winston
C14 Fingers • **C15** Bart
Final score ☐

66 THE DOCTOR'S GUESTS

A1 Kenneth Kendall • **A2** Gareth Hunt • **A3** John
Cleese • **A4** Jason Connery • **A5** Alexei Sayle
B6 Pauline Collins • **B7** Faith Brown • **B8** Sarah
Greene • **B9** Leslie Grantham • **B10** Fulton Mackay
C11 Hale and Pace • **C12** Tony Adams (Adam Chance)
C13 June Brown (Dot Cotton) • **C14** Jonathan Morris
C15 Geoff Hinsliff (Don Brennan)
Final score ☐

67 TRAIN OF THOUGHT

A1 Idris the dragon • **A2** Jones the Steam • **A3** Red
A4 Dai Station • **A5** Wales • **B6** *Union Pacific*
B7 To sing in the choir • **B8** Christopher Trace
B9 Evans the Song • **B10** *The 6.5 Special*
C11 John Adams and Patrick Whitehouse
C12 Jeff Morrow • **C13** E. Nesbit • **C14** Bernard Cribbins
C15 The Merioneth and Llantisilly Rail Traction
Company Limited
Final score ☐

68 TIME TO GO HOME

A1 The gardener • **A2** A guinea pig • **A3** Mr Benn
A4 Emily • **A5** Parsley • **B6** Madeleine
B7 Captain Snort • **B8** Joe • **B9** Bear • **B10** Pugh, Pugh,
Barney McGrew, Cuthbert, Dibble and Grubb
C11 Old Slowcoach • **C12** Louise Cochrane
C13 Mr Rumpling • **C14** The Mexican Hat Dance
C15 Janette Scott

Final score ☐

Remember, A questions are worth one point, B are
worth two and C are worth three. Crosswords and
wordsearches are not included.

Total score ☐

JUDGEMENT DAY

If you scored less than 250: I bet you're thinking, "Why
didn't I crib from *The Golden Age of Children's
Television*?"

250-750: Very impressive. Clearly if you were ever
mugged by a Pingwing, you'd be able to give an
extremely accurate description to the police

750-1,500: Excellent. You show no signs of growing up.

1,500-2,006: Nobody likes a clever dick.

The Golden Age of Children's Television is available from all good bookshops or through mail order. To order copies of the book, or for further information on all Titan's film and TV publications, please send a large stamped SAE to: **Titan Books Mail Order, 19 Valentine Place, London SE1 8QH.**
Please quote reference QB.

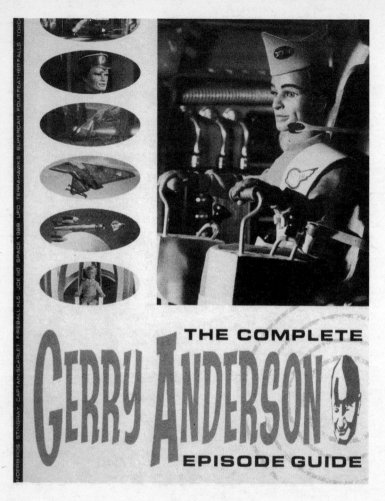

THE COMPLETE

GERRY ANDERSON

EPISODE GUIDE

The Gerry Anderson Episode Guide is also available from Titan Books Mail Order. For mail order details please see page 143.